THE UNITED STATES NUCLEAR NAVY

⚓

THE WATTS HISTORIES OF
THE UNITED STATES NAVY

⚓

THE UNITED STATES
NUCLEAR NAVY

⚓

Herbert J. Gimpel

COMMANDER, U.S.N. (RET.)

080725

FRANKLIN WATTS, INC.
575 Lexington Avenue, New York, N. Y. 10022

ACKNOWLEDGMENTS

THE STORY of nuclear power in the Navy includes many facets of this new form of energy. The Navy has been a leader in applying nuclear power and in dealing with the associated radiation safety and fallout. The work of the Manhattan District, the AEC, other branches of the armed forces, and American industry have also made notable contributions in advancing nuclear techniques.

Since the subject of this book is *The United States Nuclear Navy*, those aspects of nuclear power which are related to the U. S. Navy will necessarily be emphasized. In so doing, it is not intended to minimize the contributions or outstanding efforts of other organizations. The Navy's early efforts in fostering the growth of nuclear power have been vigorous, bold and progressive. It is hoped that this book will do justice to the early foresight, the vigorous pursuit of nuclear propulsion after World War II, and the continuing effort to improve the world's greatest Navy through nuclear power, along with the many technical advances which must keep pace with the nuclear age.

In telling this story, the cooperation of many people has been required. I am particularly grateful to: Rear Adm. Eugene P. Wilkinson, whose guidance and counsel proved invaluable; S. J. (Joe) Wornom, Jr., Manager of Public Relations for Electric Boat Division of General Dynamics Corporation, who was so generous with his help and photographs; John Lister of the Technical Information Division of NRL, who devoted much time in arranging interviews and escorting me around the Laboratory; J. Bruce Burris on the staff of the Joint Committee on Atomic Energy, who provided useful records of Congressional Hearings; Lt. Comdr. Dan Dagle of the Magazine and Book Branch, Department of Defense Public Affairs Office, whose telephone number was memorized and often used; Comdr. Ken

Wade, and later Lt. Bob Sims, Information Officers for Special Projects, who so generously provided information and photographs of the Polaris program; Lt. Comdr. Hugh Golightly, Information Officer for ONR, whose resourcefulness seems inexhaustible; and Lt. Comdr. Charles F. Tedford, Radiobiologist at the Naval Medical School, who was especially helpful in explaining the labyrinth of nuclear medical facilities at NNMC.

Other officers at NNMC who proved most helpful were: Capt. J. H. Stover, M.C., Commanding Officer, U.S. Naval Medical School; Capt. R. F. Dobbins, M.C., Director, Department of Nuclear Medicine; Capt. R. K. Skow, Radiation Safety Officer, NNMC; Comdr. John H. Ebersole, M.C., Acting Director, Radiation Exposure Evaluation Laboratory; and Capt. John H. Schulte, Director, Special Weapons Defense Division, Bureau of Medicine and Surgery.

I have always suspected that the skippers of our nuclear submarines were the finest group of people on earth. Expanding my acquaintance with them through research on this book confirmed that suspicion. Among those who contributed their help were: Capt. Paul L. Lacy, Jr., former commanding officer (CO) of the USS *Ethan Allen* (Blue) and later Special Projects Office; Capt. William W. Behrens, former CO of the USS *Skipjack*, later with MLF; Comdr. Walt Dedrick, former CO of the USS *Thomas A. Edison* (Gold) and later with Submarine Warfare Division, Naval Operations; Comdr. Charles D. Grojean, CO of the USS *Thomas A. Edison* (Gold); Comdr. George P. Steele, CO of the USS *Daniel Boone* (Blue); Comdr. Russell McWey, former Weapons Officer of the USS *Ethan Allen* (Blue); and Comdr. R. A. Harris, Assistant Officer in Charge, U.S.N. Submarine School, New London, Connecticut.

Although they are not rewarded with fame and fortune, such as our society may lavish on a rock-and-roll singer, the scientists in our laboratories are the spark plugs of progress. Some of the research projects at NRL are bound to make a layman feel like Alice in Wonderland. Those who were most helpful in their specialized fields were: Dr. Wayne C. Hall, Associate Director of Research for Nucleonics; Dr. Peter King, Associate Director of Research for Materials; John I. Hoover, Nucleonics Division (Radioactivity); Dr. R. E. Johnson, Chemistry Division; Dr. A. C. Kolb, Radiation Division (Plasma Physics); R. E. Ruskin, Atmosphere and Astrophysics Division; and Robert A. Harmon, the reference expert at the NRL Library.

Many others contributed in various ways to help make this book complete and authentic. Notable among them were: Comdr. C. W. Mallory, Director, Nuclear Power Division, Bureau of Yards and Docks; Comdr. C. H. Klindworth, Head of Information Liaison Office, Bureau of Naval Personnel; Richard C. Bassett, Technical Information representative for the Bureau of Ships; T. J. Mathews, Head, Technical Information Division, U. S. Naval Radiological Defense Laboratory, San Francisco; G. I. "Dick" Voran, Assistant Public Information Officer, Navy Electronics Laboratory, San Diego; Richard B. Yale, Jr., General Atomics Division, General Dynamics Corp., San Diego; Sydney Porter, Jr., Radiation Safety Officer, AFRRI, Bethesda, Maryland; Paul Corona, Department of Defense, Public Affairs, Pictorial Branch; Fred Meigs, Navy Department Library; Lt. Comdr. H. G. Karsten, Information Officer, USS *Enterprise;* Lt. Thomas Coyne, Information Officer, USS *Long Beach;* and Lt. (jg) R. W. Epstein, Information Officer, USS *Bainbridge.*

One short paragraph is not adequate to express my appreciation for the invaluable help I received from my wife, Ruth, who line for line and page for page, edited and typed the manuscript. When added to her exciting experience of handling the controls of a nuclear submarine at sea, she now qualifies for her "twin-dolphin pin" and a gold star for the best secretary a writer could have.

—HERBERT J. GIMPEL

Contents

⚓

To
Vice Admiral H. G. Rickover,
who has done more
to advance our U.S. nuclear Navy
than any other man in the twentieth century

Preface

I COULD NOT have undertaken the writing of *The United States Nuclear Navy* if I had known less about the subject. I might not have written it had I known more. Through the help of many experts, I have just completed a most enlightening "postgraduate course" in applied nuclear physics. Nevertheless, steaming ahead so freely on nuclear power into the realm of history, science, medicine, and world affairs, all the opinions expressed in this book are those of the author and are not necessarily to be construed as official or reflecting the views of the Defense Department or any of the armed services.

—Commander Herbert J. Gimpel, U.S.N. (Ret.)
Bethesda, Maryland

ONE

Dawn of the Nuclear Age

As THE B-29 droned four thousand feet above the Pacific, one man, cramped and alone in the darkness of the bomb bay, held history in his blackened and abraded fingers. Too much depended on his sense of touch to wear gloves. The finely machined gadget which absorbed his full concentration was the culmination of years of discovery by the world's leading scientists—a crash project which took the efforts of more than 540,000 people, and cost two billion dollars. It was August 6, 1945. The B-29, named *Enola Gay,* was headed for Hiroshima with the world's first atomic bomb.

The man whose shoulders bore this heavy burden carried the code name of "Judge" in the Manhattan Project. His friends called him "Deac." On the rolls of the U. S. Navy, he was then Capt. William S. Parsons. The story leading to his presence in the bomb bay of the *Enola Gay* with the first atomic bomb is as dramatic as any battle of World War II, and perhaps more important. The cataclysmic explosion which ignited over Hiroshima stunned the world and changed it profoundly.

Captain Parsons was one of two naval officers destined to be closely associated with the first atomic bombs. The other was Comdr. Frederick L. Ashworth. Both were graduates of the Naval Academy at Annapolis, and both later became admirals. They were hand-picked for important roles in the Manhattan Project, and had something special to offer in knowledge and experience in delivering the first atomic bombs.

[3]

Before his selection for work with the Manhattan District at Los Alamos, New Mexico, in June, 1943, Captain Parsons had been the experimental officer at the Naval Proving Ground, Dahlgren, Virginia, with additional duty as special assistant to Dr. Vannevar Bush in connection with developing the proximity fuze. He introduced the proximity fuze to the Pacific Fleet in January, 1943, and witnessed its first use in battle from the cruiser USS *Helena.*

At the Los Alamos Laboratory, where the atomic bombs were developed, he served as associate director of the Ordnance Division and finally as the officer in charge of the Overseas Technical Group of the Los Alamos Scientific Laboratory. After observing the first atomic test explosion in New Mexico, he flew to the Marianas as weaponeer and bomb commander on the first atomic bomb drop. The next nuclear explosion would not be a test!

Commander Ashworth, an aviation ordnance expert, learned about the atomic bomb one Sunday afternoon in June, 1944, at Wendover Field, Utah. Norman Ramsey, a special assistant to Maj. Gen. Leslie R. Groves, drove him to a far and quiet corner of the air base and, in the "cloak and dagger" secrecy required, explained his part in the project and the need for utmost secrecy.

Working with the B-29s of the 509th Composite Group at Wendover Field, Commander Ashworth became familiar with the problems involved and he also became acquainted with his co-workers in the Army Air Force. In December, he was ordered to Washington by Adm. Ernest J. King. The time had come to inform some of the key commanders in the Pacific about plans for the atomic bomb. A memo, outlining the availability of the bomb, from General Groves to the Army Chief of Staff, had been appropriately read and approved by the top military commanders in Washington, including Secretary of War Stimson and President Roosevelt. One part of the memo, dated December 30, 1944, read:

"I also feel that it would be advisable for Admiral Nimitz to be informed of our general plans in order that we will be assured the essential Navy assistance in the area. This could be accomplished by means of a letter from Admiral King to Admiral Nimitz to be delivered by one of the naval officers now on duty in my command."

Commander Ashworth was selected as the naval officer "now on duty in my command" to deliver the letter to Admiral Nimitz, Commander of the Pacific Fleet, headquartered at Guam. When Commander Ashworth departed from Washington with this letter, he also carried instructions to find a suitable operating base in the Pacific for the 509th.

With the war in Europe grinding to a halt, it was clear that Japan would be the logical country on which to drop the first A-bomb. The time scale called for the bomb to be ready some time in August, by which time Germany was calculated to have already collapsed. Furthermore, the "strategic" bombing concept in Germany, which acquired such euphemistic labels as "carpet bombing" and "saturation bombing," left few major cities with any large building intact. To drop an A-bomb over the existing debris would be highly unstrategic. Therefore, Japan was destined for the first A-bomb in the hope that it would quickly end the war in the Pacific.

In February, 1945, Commander Ashworth arrived at the headquarters of the Commander in Chief of the Pacific Fleet on Guam. It was the first time that Admiral Nimitz had heard about the proposed A-bombing in August. However, Gen. Douglas MacArthur, who had been the Supreme Commander in the Pacific for over three years, was not informed about the existence of the A-bomb or its planned use in his area until August 1, 1945—five days before the bombing of Hiroshima!

When Commander Ashworth explained the impressive effort in making the A-bomb, Admiral Nimitz said: "Son, I guess I was just born twenty years too soon." He appointed his Chief of Staff, Vice Adm. C. H. McMorris, as his atomic coordinator.

Commander Ashworth made a survey of the Mariana Islands to select the most suitable place for basing the 509th. This group consisted of specially selected officers and men of the Army Air Force. Assigned to the group were fifteen B-29 bombers, stripped of all armament except for two .50-caliber machine guns as a tail stinger. The lack of armament lightened the B-29s in order to give them increased speed and a fast getaway after releasing the extremely heavy A-bomb.

Even though Guam was larger, better developed, and had better port facilities, Commander Ashworth decided to pick Tinian Island. It was closer to Japan, and the fact that it was small, not as well developed, and less populated made it more desirable for security control. Another important consideration was the construction of North Field on Tinian, with its four runways—the biggest bomber base in the Pacific. He chose a site bordering North Field for locating three Quonset huts for bomb assembly—prototypes of three huts which had been built and tested at the Naval Ordnance Test Station at Inyokern, California.

By the end of April, the 509th started its move from Wendover Field to its advance staging base on Tinian. About two hundred men were added to the group, every one very carefully selected by Commander Ashworth. They formed the 1st Ordnance Squadron (Special Aviation)—the most secret part of the 509th—under Major Charles F. H. Begg. The men in this group were bound by the strictest security regulations. One man could not discuss his work with another and no information about his job could be written to his family. They traveled as a unit, separate from other troops, and were always accompanied by intelligence officers.

Transporting the components of the A-bombs to Tinian was anything but a routine job. The U-235 and plutonium from Oak Ridge, Tennessee, used in the two A-bombs, was the end product of a gigantic effort of the Manhattan Project in people, talent and money, not to mention the fifteen thousand tons of silver borrowed from the U. S. Treasury to make the ribbons of silver coils for the electromagnetic separation plant.

To carry the first explosive batch of U-235 to Tinian, the two people selected for the escort job were Maj. Robert R. Furman, a graduate engineer from Princeton, and Lt. Col. James F. Nolan, a physician at the Los Alamos Laboratory hospital. They were to fly to San Francisco with their precious cargo, and take it from there to Tinian on board the heavy cruiser USS *Indianapolis*. Their "package" turned out to be something on the order of a country milk can with a curved handle on top, one and a half feet in diameter and almost two feet high. When Dr. Nolan tried to lift it, the can seemed welded to the floor—thanks to a couple hundred pounds of lead lining the inside, used for radiation protection.

At San Francisco, the two escorts, with their charge, were met by an impressive security guard for the trip to the Navy Yard at Hunters Point where the can was delivered to the Commandant. Here they reported to Rear Adm. William R. Purnell, the Navy coordinator who had long been associated with the A-bomb project. He had already carefully briefed Capt. Charles B. McVay, commanding officer of the cruiser *Indianapolis*, concerning the importance of his top-secret cargo without divulging anything of its nature.

Before sunrise on July 16, 1945, two sturdy sailors walked up the after gangway with "the thing" slung over their shoulders by a crowbar placed through the handle. At the same time, a long crate enclosing one of the casings for the atomic bomb was being hoisted aboard by one of the ship's cranes. The crate aroused much speculation among the ship's company of the *Indianapolis*. Most of them guessed that it was "some kind of secret weapon." Although they had no idea what kind of secret weapon, they were absolutely correct!

The can with the mass of lead surrounding the uranium-235 was fastened securely to the deck of one of the ship's staterooms. Straps, looped under the handle of the can, were secured with eyebolts welded to the deck and padlocked. Major Furman and Dr. Nolan stood four-hour watches over their charge during the entire voyage.

The ship made a fast run to Tinian with a stop at Pearl Harbor to top-off fuel bunkers.

On the morning of July 26, the *Indianapolis* anchored off Tinian Island, where an LST came alongside to transfer the crate from the cruiser's deck. During this operation, Nolan and Furman had their important cargo transferred to a motor launch back aft. Once ashore, they were met by a pick-up truck which finally deposited the U-235 to the bomb assembly hut at North Field.

Mission accomplished! As for the cruiser *Indianapolis*, however, it was her last mission to be accomplished—four days later she was torpedoed and sunk by a Japanese submarine. We can only speculate on how the course of history might have changed if *Indianapolis* had been sunk a week earlier, because the U-235 she carried was the only batch available at the time she steamed under the Golden Gate Bridge from San Francisco.

With the day of the first atomic bombing drawing near, Captain Parsons, Commander Ashworth, Tom Farrell and Lt. Col. Paul W. Tibbets, Jr., met with Gen. Curtis E. LeMay to plan details of the operation. It was agreed that seven B-29s would be used. Three of them would proceed to the target cities—Hiroshima, Kokura and Nagasaki—to report on the weather. Their orders directed—and Dr. J. R. Oppenheimer insisted—that the bomb drop be made visually rather than by radar. This meant that good weather and good visibility had to prevail over the target city.

Two B-29s were to accompany Lt. Colonel Tibbets, flying the *Enola Gay* with the bomb, for scientific observation and photography. The seventh plane was a spare to be positioned at Iwo Jima in case the *Enola Gay* developed mechanical trouble. In the event of major trouble, a vast net of air-sea rescue units were laid on, including submarines and Navy seaplanes.

The B-29 crews involved in the operation were given a briefing on the morning of August 4 by Captain Parsons. He showed them movies of the first atomic blast which was tested on July 16 at

Alamogordo, New Mexico. He cautioned against flying through the cloud formed after the explosion because of radioactivity. They were not told that it was an atomic weapon—only that it was a "new" weapon. The fantastic magnitude of the explosion on film was most impressive and made the airmen realize why they had spent so much time practicing the steep-diving and get-away turns at high altitude.

Farrell, who was General Groves' representative on the scene, worked out a private code of twenty-eight possible eventualities of what might happen over the target. By using the numbers on the code, Captain Parsons could quickly inform Farrell on Tinian, and he would relay the information to General Groves in Washington.

Realizing the historical importance of the occasion, Lt. Colonel Tibbets gave his B-29 a name instead of using just the number "82" or the Army Air Force serial number. He named his B-29 *Enola Gay*, after his mother back in the little town of Glidden, Iowa.

As the atomic bomb was loaded in the bomb bay of *Enola Gay*, and the plane was rolled out in position to await take-off the next day, Captain Parsons took Farrell aside to discuss an important detail. A number of B-29s had crashed recently on take-off, and the explosion of bombs, burning of gasoline and wild spraying of machine-gun bullets resulted in a ghastly scene. If the *Enola Gay* should crash on take-off, there would be no witnesses, for half of the island would be blown up. To solve the problem, Captain Parsons suggested putting off the final assembly until after the plane had taken off. When Farrell asked if he knew how, Captain Parsons said: "No, but I've got all day and night to learn."

Months before, Lt. Comdr. Francis Birch, who was Captain Parsons' ordnance assistant, had developed a double plug system which would permit arming the bomb in flight. Although the idea was vetoed at Los Alamos, Birch had devised the system on his own. It permitted inserting a conventional explosive in the tail of the bomb which would drive the two pieces of U-235 together. By separating them, an atomic explosion could not occur.

[9]

His work cut out for him, Captain Parsons toiled all day in the heat of the bomb bay, squeezed into a cramped position behind the bomb. Aided by a flashlight in the darkness of the bomb bay, he practiced the assembly many times. By the time he had it perfected, his hands were cut and sore from the sharply tooled parts. As a result of his courage and ingenuity, there was much less apprehension when *Enola Gay* roared down the runway at North Field. She almost reached the end of the crushed-coral strip before finally lifting off at 2:45 A.M., Tinian time, on August 6, 1945.

The atomic bomb was on its way to Japan! In order of priority, the targets were: Hiroshima, Kokura and Nagasaki. The city of Hiroshima had the grim honor. The city lay below, a few clouds drifting by casting patches of shade which moved across the landscape.

En route, Captain Parson squeezed once more into the bomb bay while Lt. Maurice Jeppson, of the flight crew, held a flashlight and handed tools to him. Occasionally Parsons spoke over the plane's intercom system to the pilot, Tibbets, assuring him that all was going well. In about half an hour the job was done. Parsons climbed out of the bomb bay, and checked the console which showed that all of the bomb's electrical circuits were working properly.

As they approached the target, Captain Parsons stood behind Tibbets. Through a large opening in the clouds, a city appeared below—Hiroshima! The bomb bay doors opened automatically from the signal on the bombing panel, and the bomb, nicknamed "Little Boy," tumbled out and plunged down on target.

Enola Gay, freed of its five-ton load, leaped upward momentarily and Tibbets rolled over into a tight, descending turn to gain speed and distance for what was about to happen in 43 seconds.

To prevent being blinded by the huge flash of light, all members of the flight crew were reminded to make sure their goggles were on. The flash of light became a ball of fire about a half mile across with an incredible temperature of a hundred million degrees at its center.

The intense heat, devastating shock wave and deadly radiation which followed left Hiroshima a dead city, struck with a weird and strange force unprecedented in its destructive power. The death and destruction which followed from this one bomb shocked the world. However, its intended purpose was to produce such an effect on the Japanese that it would precipitate a surrender and bring World War II to an end.

The shock effect can hardly have made much of an impression on Tokyo, for on the following day the morning newspaper *Asahi,* in Tokyo, produced the grand champion of understatements. It read: "Hiroshima was attacked August 6 by two B-29 planes, which dropped incendiary bombs. The planes invaded the city around 7:50 A.M. It seems that some damage was caused to the city and its vicinity."

Hardened by years of war, Japan paid little heed to the Potsdam Declaration which was issued on July 26, 1945, and signed by President Truman, Britain's Clement Attlee, and China's Chiang Kai-shek. This was, in effect, an ultimatum to surrender unconditionally or face "prompt and utter destruction." The atomic bomb, although not mentioned, was the "prompt and utter destruction" referred to. The ultimatum was rejected. There was no indication from Japan of an intention to surrender after the disaster at Hiroshima. Meanwhile, the second bomb was being readied.

On August 9, the second atomic bomb was on its way to Japan. It was a plutonium explosive even more powerful than the explosion over Hiroshima. Commander Ashworth was in charge of this bomb as the B-29 headed for Nagasaki. In case it was thought that the first atomic blast was a one-time event, the disaster at Nagasaki punctuated the bombing of Hiroshima, telling the Japanese in a clear, unmistakable demonstration that continuing the war was utterly futile.

Spread underneath the two mushroom-shaped clouds were appalling scenes of death and devastation. Following the blinding flash of light from the atomic explosions, other destructive energy was given off in the form of heat, pressure (blast) and radiation.

One of the reports made by the U. S. Strategic Bombing Survey read in part: "The duration of the flash was only a fraction of a second, but it was sufficiently intense to cause third degree burns to exposed human skin up to a distance of a mile. In the immediate area of ground zero (the point directly under the explosion), the heat charred human bodies beyond recognition. The blast which followed the flash was of sufficient force to press in the roofs of reinforced concrete structures and to flatten completely all less sturdy structures.

"The plutonium bomb used at Nagasaki," the report continued, "had a fifteen percent greater radius of destruction than the uranium-235 bomb used at Hiroshima. The lower casualties at Nagasaki were mainly due to the uneven terrain which shielded parts of the city from the effects of the bomb."

Much more dramatic than structural damage was the human suffering in terms of the dead, the crippled, and the badly burned. The disruption of life under the two atomic explosions marked the spot where two cities died for a while.

The opinions of intelligent people all over the world varied regarding the justification of the atom-bombing of Hiroshima and Nagasaki. Some thought the bombings were barbaric and unjustified; others contended that they saved many lives on both sides by ending the war. A little-discussed benefit to Japan was the advantage of bringing about a Japanese surrender before Russia could enter the war against her in any way except as a token gesture. As a result, a struggle for authority was avoided with Russia over Japan, and Russian expansionist goals were frustrated.

Perhaps the mushroom-shaped clouds over Hiroshima and Nagasaki had a silver lining: by surrendering to the United States, Japan was saved from being torn apart and divided into zones by the Communists as was the case in Germany. The military reasons for dropping the bombs may have been outweighed by the political advantage of keeping the paws of the big Russian bear out of Japan's rice bowl.

The pros and cons concerning the use of atomic bombs in World War II will go on for decades, and perhaps the issue will never be completely settled. Yet one thing is certain—the huge fireballs from these atomic explosions signaled the dawn of the nuclear age, however bloody-red the dawn.

Prying the Lid From Pandora's Box

IT WAS a warm spring day in 1939 as a group of scientists, their shirt sleeves rolled up, gathered in a hot, muggy office along the Potomac, just downriver from Washington, D. C. The heat went unnoticed as they listened intently to the man who was speaking. He was Dr. Ross Gunn, Chief Physicist at the Naval Research Laboratory. Dr. Gunn tapped on a glass of water and said: "There is enough energy in this glass of water to drive the *Queen Mary* across the Atlantic Ocean."

His audience was composed of his fellow scientists at the laboratory who formed a small part of the world's scientific community awakening to the fantastic energy locked within the atom. Finding the key to the lock would open a vast new source of energy. It would also lift the lid from a Pandora's box of mischief whose control would puzzle the world for decades, if not for centuries.

Releasing the cosmic forces locked within the nuclei of atoms was not a one-man or one-nation effort. It was an international effort spread over many years of scientific research. To see this drama unfold, we must look back at the scientific highlights, as well as the U. S. Navy's early interest in nuclear power which played a part in the atomic explosions of August, 1945.

As early as 1896, Henri Becquerel's discovery of radioactivity gave first evidence that there was a source of energy in atoms in addition to its chemical energy. Pierre and Marie Curie, in Paris, followed with the discovery of the new chemical element, radium.

Across the English Channel, Ernest Rutherford, better known as Lord Rutherford, discovered the nucleus of the atom in 1911. Eight years later, he discovered how to change one chemical into another by means of helium acting on nitrogen to produce hydrogen. In the process, nuclear energy was released. Although it was not put to practical use, it was a step forward in extracting power from the atom. With keen foresight, Lord Rutherford wrote to a friend that the significance of this experiment might one day be of greater influence on history than World War I, which had just ended.

In the fall of 1938, with the clouds of World War II hanging over Europe, Otto Hahn and Fritz Strassman, in Berlin, succeeded in splitting uranium atoms by bombarding them with neutrons at the Kaiser Wilhelm Institute for Chemistry. After the bombardment they discovered barium in the uranium mass. Lise Meitner, who had formerly worked with Hahn before fleeing from Berlin to Stockholm, properly guessed how barium was produced—by the splitting of the uranium atom into two parts to create the low-atomic-numbered barium. The resultant release of energy followed Albert Einstein's famous equation—$E = mc^2$, where E is energy, m is mass, and c is the speed of light.

In Italy, Dr. Enrico Fermi was busy during the pre-war years working on slow-moving neutrons, and the formation of a series of artificial atoms. It is notable that this international fraternity of scientists was not only free with the knowledge of its new discoveries, but eager to pass these findings on to each other.

The difficult atmosphere of wartime Europe attracted many scientists to the United States where the laboratories were fairly crackling with scientific rapport. This resulted in the Danish physicist Niels Bohr working with Dr. J. A. Wheeler, of Princeton, in developing the theory of the fission process. The Hungarian scientist Leo Szilard, at Columbia University, worked with physicists W. H. Zinn, H. L. Anderson, Enrico Fermi and H. B. Hanstein on similar experiments with nuclear fission. There are many others, such as Dr. Edward Teller and Dr. Ernest O. Lawrence at Berkeley, California, whose contributions were notable in nuclear physics. Working together,

European and American physicists were progressively unlocking the tremendous energy within the atom.

It was Dr. Fermi who supervised an historic event on December 2, 1942, on the squash court under the grandstand of the University of Chicago's Stagg Field. Using piles of graphite in which uranium metal and oxide were embedded, the scientists of the Manhattan District produced the world's first controlled nuclear chain reaction in which nuclear fission was started, sustained and stopped. This must be considered a signal event in the dawn of the nuclear age. In less than three years, the world would learn of the tremendous explosive energy locked within the nucleus of atoms.

With the world at war, the submicroscopic atom became, in fact, a huge sleeping monster whose destructive powers were unprecedented. We can only wonder whether the first use of a nuclear chain reaction might have been for the benefit of mankind instead of for his destruction, had the secrets of nuclear fission chosen a less awkward time in the world's history to emerge from the unknown. Unfortunately, the world was not at peace, it was at war. It was therefore only natural that nuclear power first should be used as an instrument of war.

In March, 1939, at a meeting attended by scientists and officers of the U. S. Navy, Dr. Fermi had suggested the possibility of achieving a uranium chain reaction which might be either controlled or be of an explosive nature. Although a nuclear chain reaction had not yet been achieved, the scientists present thought mostly in terms of an explosive which would release a million times more energy per pound than a conventional explosive. The Navy men at the meeting were intrigued with the possibilities of the controlled chain reaction for propelling ships.

Following the meeting with Dr. Fermi in Washington, the chief physicist at the Naval Research Laboratory requested funds to carry on nuclear research. Rear Adm. Harold G. Bowen, Chief of the Bureau of Ships (as it is now called), approved the amount of $2,000 for preliminary exploratory work on developing atomic energy. It was most significant that this money, spent by the Navy, was the first expenditure by the United States Government for work on atomic energy.

Admiral Bowen's enthusiasm over the possibilities of nuclear power was fortunate because he subsequently became Director of the Naval Research Laboratory, and later was assigned as the Chief of the newly created Office of Naval Research in 1945.

Nuclear propulsion, although fascinating to a number of people in the Navy, had to await the end of World War II. The seemingly impossible job was then given to a Navy captain who was destined to become the Robert Fulton of the twentieth century—Hyman G. Rickover.

Because of the importance of the Navy's work on isotope separation at the Naval Research Laboratory, and its substantial contribution to the first atomic explosions, it deserves some attention. The heroes in this exciting drama almost slipped by the recorded pages of history because of the wartime secrecy under which they were forced to work. By the time the sensational explosions over Hiroshima and Nagasaki had awed the world and hastened the end of World War II, other events had overshadowed the pioneer work in atomic energy at the Naval Research Laboratory.

While first working on his method of isotope separation at the Carnegie Institution of Washington, Dr. Philip Abelson was under contract by the NRL. In July, 1941, he moved the entire project to the Naval Research Laboratory, and worked directly for the Navy. Assisted by another scientist, John I. Hoover, investigations proceeded on various methods of applying the liquid thermal diffusion method of separating isotopes of uranium. The end product was uranium enriched in the fissionable U-235 isotope.

In developing a pilot plant for isotope separation, a number of problems in chemistry and engineering had to be solved. It was found that temperature conditions and the length of the columns through which the fluid passed were important. Studies of uranium compounds showed that uranium hexafluoride was the only substance then known which answered their purpose. Uranium was expensive, and fluorine was unavailable commercially, so they devised a method of producing uranium hexafluoride.

After making corrosion studies on various metals, the scientists built a pilot plant at the NRL which was completed in November, 1942. It was successful in producing enriched uranium after six months of operation. During this period, the scientific staff working on experimental isotope separation was increased to include William Blatt, Robert Ruskin, Edward Drott, Jr., and Waldo Whybrew. Dr. Nathan Rosen, of the University of North Carolina, assisted with theoretical studies, and the University of Virginia Physics Department provided mass-spectrographic analysis.

All the information concerning progress with uranium isotope separation was passed on to the Manhattan District when it was established to develop the first atomic bombs. A report submitted by the NRL in January, 1943, outlined the advantages of an enriched chain reactor, and stated that a large thermal diffusion plant was not required for necessary isotope separation. In August, 1943, a committee was appointed by the Manhattan District to investigate the liquid thermal diffusion process at the NRL. The committee, consisting of Lyman Briggs, Harold Urey, E. V. Murphree, and W. L. Lewis, with Karl Cohen and W. I. Thompson as technical advisers, favored support on work toward improving the efficiency of the process.

The thermal diffusion installation at the NRL showed that it was cheaper to construct than any other proposed separation plant, and could be built in a short time. The big problem was supplying the enormous amounts of steam required to make it work. At the Philadelphia Navy Yard, facilities were available for making plenty of high-pressure steam on a large-scale operation at the Naval Boiler and Turbine Laboratory. Also, building space was available and cooling water was obtainable.

Rear Adm. Earle Mills, Assistant Chief of the Bureau of Ships, signed the authorization to build the plant on November 17, 1943, and construction started early in January, 1944. The Philadelphia plant was built by the NRL with the assistance of Samuel Weir of the Turbine and Boiler Laboratory. Some thought was given to its being a model plant in the event that the Manhattan District might decide to use the liquid thermal diffusion method in its atomic bomb project.

The Philadelphia plant was divided into two parts—the steam and water works, and the uranium process area. The former was provided by enlisted men at the Naval Boiler and Turbine Laboratory under Capt. C. A. Bonvillian. The laboratory was under Rear Adm. A. H. Van Keuren, and later Commodore H. A. Schade, with project officers Capt. R. H. Gibbs and Capt. J. B. Cochran.

The process area was staffed largely by technical personnel, officers and enlisted men who were selected for their scientific backgrounds. They worked under the technical direction of the two civilian supervisors, Abelson and Hoover. The technical capabilities of the uniformed personnel were more important than rank and, at times, clashed with Navy protocol. It is notable that Abelson and Hoover put in some long, weird hours, many of them without compensation. Many of our wartime battles were waged and won in laboratories as well as in combat.

By June, 1944, when the Philadelphia installation was almost finished, J. R. Oppenheimer learned of the progress being made and was aware of its important contribution in helping to feed the electromagnetic separation plant at Oak Ridge, Tennessee. It was extremely important that the production of this plant be increased. The potentialities of the liquid thermal diffusion plant in bringing about this increase prompted Oppenheimer to call it to the attention of Maj. Gen. L. R. Groves, who was in charge of the Manhattan District. As a result, on June 15 a reviewing committee visited the plant at Philadelphia. The committee's favorable report to General Groves spurred the decision to build a liquid thermal diffusion plant at Oak Ridge. A steam plant had already been installed there for the gaseous diffusion process which had not been sufficiently developed at that time for the engineering phase, so plenty of steam was available.

Later in June, General Groves, together with Richard Tolman, W. I. Thompson, and Lt. Col. M. C. Fox, visited the NRL to gather all available information on the isotope separation process for the Manhattan Project. At that time, blueprints were turned over to them, and General Groves gave instructions to build an exact copy of the Philadelphia plant at Oak Ridge. Thanks to tremendous effort and the outstanding teamwork of civilian and military workers, construction of the plant at Oak Ridge began on July 6, 1944. By the end of October it was already producing enriched uranium for the Manhattan Project. When supplied to the electromagnetic plant, this enriched uranium increased the production of fissionable U-235 by about four times the rate of that using natural uranium.

A simplified description of the liquid thermal diffusion process may be of interest. The thermal diffusion takes place in a series of long, slender columns, each consisting of three concentric tubes. The center tube is heated by steam passing through it from top to bottom. Around the center tube is another which carries the uranium hexafluoride. On the outside is the third tube through which cold water passes. Within the uranium hexafluoride, the U-235 isotope, being lighter than the common, heavier, and more abundant U-238 isotope, moves toward the hot inner wall because of thermal diffusion. At the same time, the heat from the inner wall sets up a current by convection in which the material along the hot wall flows upward while the material along the cold outer wall is carried downward. The material along the inner wall, which has a slightly higher concentration of

U-235, collects at the top where it is skimmed off. The product of this partial separation of U-235 from U-238 is called enriched uranium.

During part of 1944 and 1945, the NRL's team at Philadelphia shipped 5,034 pounds of enriched uranium to the Manhattan Project at Oak Ridge—a substantial contribution, indeed, to the atomic explosions of 1945.

The secrecy maintained on the entire Manhattan Project during the war is amazing, considering how many people were working on it without knowing what it was they were producing. Needless to say, men who came with the express trucks which picked up the enriched uranium at the Philadelphia Navy Yard had no idea of what they were hauling.

"They would throw the containers of enriched uranium on the back of the truck with the same abandon as throwing in a box of scrap metal," Hoover observed. However, it was noticed that the shipments picked up after the announcement of the A-bomb over Hiroshima, were handled with delicate apprehension. It was not the least bit comforting when a pick-up was made while the uranium shipment was still warm. As the enriched uranium cooled, it cracked off the sides of the container with a ticking sound not unlike a time bomb.

The pilot plant at Philadelphia continued to produce enriched uranium for the Manhattan Project throughout World War II. In terms of money and man-hours, the contribution of the NRL was a small percentage of the multibillion-dollar overall effort involving over a half-million people. However, the NRL played an important part in advancing nuclear know-how during a moment of history when time was short and the stakes were high.

As calculated, the atomic bombs dropped over Japan hastened the end of the war. Although Japan was already crumbling under heavy losses, and was cut off from vital supplies at sea, the atomic bombs drew the curtain on the tragic drama waged across the vast stage of the Pacific.

Perhaps it is not too late to acknowledge the important contribution toward victory made by our legions of the laboratories which helped pry the lid from Pandora's box—a box which no mortal now can close.

⚓

THREE

Operation Crossroads

HIROSHIMA and Nagasaki were now past history. The greatest war the world had ever known had come to a cataclysmic, catastrophic end on August 14, 1945. In terms of human life lost, it had been a war with no real winners—all participants had been heavy losers.

In the postwar effort to pick up the fragments of civilization and restore a normal order of society at home and abroad, each country was left with ponderous problems. Although rebuilding smashed cities was not among the problems of the United States, she still was faced with a unique problem in postwar adjustments. She had developed a weapon of terrifying power which had annihilated two cities with a cosmic force of unprecedented violence. The United States had a bear by the tail!

The scientific achievement in developing the atomic bomb had been a monumental one. What we still did not know about the effects of nuclear explosions was to fill many books.

As early as August 28, 1945, Senator Brien McMahon, who was later to become the Chairman of the Senate's Special Committee on Atomic Energy, asked that the new bomb be tested against the Japanese naval ships we had acquired. In a speech he said: "In order to test the destructive powers of the atomic bomb against naval vessels, I would like to see these Japanese ships taken to sea and an atomic bomb dropped on them."

Lt. Gen. B. M. Giles, USA, then in Tokyo, proposed on September 14, 1945, that at least two atomic bombs be used in their destruction. Gen. H. H. Arnold, Commanding General of the Army Air Force, and a member of the Joint Chiefs of Staff, urgently requested that a number of the Japanese ships be made available to the Army Air Force for use in testing atomic bombs as well as conventional weapons.

It was Adm. Ernest J. King, then Commander in Chief of the U. S. Fleet and Chief of Naval Operations, who made the suggestion that was finally adopted. On October 16, 1945, he proposed that the Joint Chiefs of Staff control the tests, and that all interested elements of the Army and Navy participate. He recommended that one atomic explosion be detonated in the air, and another be detonated in the water. He also suggested that some of our own ships be included among those arrayed in the target area.

The tests would involve naval operations principally—Navy ships as targets, naval support, and naval construction facilities afloat and ashore, including final damage inspection and appraisal of naval ships. It was therefore decided to appoint a naval officer to command the tests—Vice Adm. W. H. P. Blandy. He was designated Commander Joint Task Force One on January 11, 1946. Admiral Blandy's charter and guidelines from the Joint Chiefs of Staff read as follows:

"1. By direction of the President, you are designated commander of a task force under the Joint Chiefs of Staff for the purpose of conducting tests for the determination of the effects of atomic explosives against naval vessels in order to appraise the strategic implications of atomic bombs including the results on naval design and tactics. You will organize a joint staff with adequate representation of land, sea, and air forces. You will include civilian scientists in your organization.

"2. The general requirements of the test will be to determine the effects of atomic explosives against ships selected to give good representation of construction of modern naval and merchant vessels suitably disposed to give a gradation of damage from maximum to minimum. It is desired to include in the tests both air detonation and underwater detonation if the latter is considered feasible. Tests

[24]

should be so arranged as to take advantage of opportunities to obtain the effects of atomic explosives against ground and air targets and to acquire scientific data of general value if this is practicable.

"3. You are authorized to deal directly with agencies of the War and Navy Department in all matters relating to the preparation for the conduct of these tests; including direct access to the Manhattan District. Usual service lines will be available for administrative and logistic support of forces assigned. . . .

"4. The Joint Chiefs of Staff will appoint as a separate agency, directly responsible to them, an evaluation board (committee) for the express purpose of evaluating the results of the tests. This board will be available to you for advice during the preparation of the tests. Appropriate sections of your organization will collaborate with this board as necessary, and you will provide it with all necessary facilities it may require to fulfill its functions.

"5. You will prepare plans for the test including selection of a suitable site which will permit accomplishment of the test with acceptable risk and minimum hazard. Your plans for the operation and final report will be submitted to the Joint Chiefs of Staff for their approval."

Up to this time, three atomic explosions had been successful—a test, Hiroshima and Nagasaki. The authority was now granted to conduct the largest-scale scientific test and evaluation operation the world had ever known.

Admiral Blandy decided to label the two bomb tests "Operation Crossroads." In many ways, it was a crossroads between the past and the future, between a plateau of scientific achievement and further progress, and certainly a crossroads in terms of decisions, questions and answers.

The answers required were to determine the array of scientific devices and instruments placed throughout the entire target area. What happens during an atomic explosion? How much of the energy goes into the pressure wave? How much converts into thermal radiation, gamma radiation, and neutron radiation? What is the force of the pressure at the center of the explosion, and how fast does it diminish in time and concentric gradations from ground zero? How fast does the shock wave travel? How strong is the suction, or rush of atmosphere back toward the center of the explosion?

The test results would determine how much damage would occur to ships, aircraft, trucks, and other equipment at various distances. What parts of ships would have to be strengthened? Do riveted or welded seams withstand the tremendous pressure better? What happens to topside structures—deckhouses, masts, guns, and superstructures? Do fuel and ammunition ignite? At what distance is the blast fatal? What are the aftereffects of radiation sickness? How long would the lethal effects of fission products remain?

The answers to these questions were designed to make our Navy, Army and Air Force better able to face the future world of atomic power. The far-reaching conclusions also extended to civil defense, medical, and other scientific fields. In particular, Operation Crossroads would answer many questions for the Navy because no ships had actually been involved in any of the three previous atomic explosions. Time and circumstances had not permitted the extensive gleaning of scientific and technical data in the atomic explosions of 1945.

Admiral Blandy's joint task force was designed to meet the special needs of the job to be performed, and eight task groups were established to execute the plans. A Joint Task Force operational and administrative staff was organized under Commodore J. A. Snackenberg, Chief of Staff, to handle the vast details concerned with personnel, public relations, military security, ship movements, communications and supply.

Task Group 1.1, known as the Technical Group, was commanded by Rear Adm. W. S. Parsons, whose sterling qualities and abilities were so heavily relied upon in the delivery of the first atomic bomb. He was also the Deputy Task Force Commander for Technical

Direction. His group included seven large laboratory ships, radio-controlled drone boats, and *LSM-60*. The latter was the ship from which the underwater atomic explosive was to be suspended.

Admiral Parsons was responsible for readying the ships, instruments, and test animals; detonating both atomic explosions; and evaluating the results of Tests A and B. Dividing the organization into logical divisions was one of his big jobs. He was assisted by Capt. Horacio Rivero, USN., and Captain Ashworth, who assisted with the delivery of the Nagasaki bomb. The technical activities were divided into two administrative groups. One was commanded by Rear Adm. T. A. Solberg, the Director of Ship Material; the other under the leadership of Dr. R. A. Sawyer, Technical Director.

The group under Admiral Solberg required the services of 10,000 men in the gigantic task of preparing the target and support ships for the tests. Involved were 149 ships; of these, 36 were large ships over 10,000 tons. The support ships had to be converted to provide additional office space and communications equipment—particularly the flagship, USS *Mt. McKinley*. On USS *Appalachian*, the press ship, accommodations included a broadcasting studio, and television and teletype equipment.

USS *Albemarle* and USS *Cumberland Sound*, carrying many scientists from Los Alamos, became huge floating laboratories. Special instruments for measuring effects of the tests required building much of the equipment on board the ships. Machinery, tools, and working spaces were needed for the scientists. Laboratories also were installed in USS *Kenneth Whiting*, USS *Wharton*, USS *Avery Island*, and the hospital ship USS *Haven*.

The ship most resembling Noah's Ark was USS *Burleson*, a floating hotel for the test animals, and equipped with several laboratories. The escort carrier, USS *Saidor*, and other ships were equipped with special photo labs. In Test B, the point-zero ship, *LSM-60*, required a special well in the deck through which the underwater atomic explosive could be lowered.

One of the most difficult projects in preparing the ships for the tests at Bikini Atoll was making them leak-proof. Since all ships leak a little, bilge pumps are used to control normal leakage. Establishing the water-tight integrity between thousands of compartments in these test ships was a task of great magnitude. With no one on board, progressive leaking in some of the older ships could possibly have sunk them without a cap pistol being fired, let alone an A-bomb. In addition to water-tightness, thousands of special mountings for gauges, recorders, cages, and other fittings had to be installed.

Shipyards everywhere contributed toward the tremendous job of ship preparation. Ships arrived from Japan, China, Guam, Okinawa, Saipan, the continental U. S., and Pearl Harbor. The cruiser *Prinz Eugen* came from Germany by way of Boston, Philadelphia, and the Panama Canal. The Japanese battleship *Nagato* arrived from Yokosuka, and the cruiser *Sakawa* from Otake, Japan. It was the largest assemblage of doomed ships in history.

Also gathering at Bikini were the largest number of scientists ever assembled in the Pacific. Among them were nuclear physicists, mathematicians, roentgenologists, chemists, spectroscopists, biologists, biophysicists, veterinarians, hematologists, piscatologists, oceanographers, geologists, seismologists, and meterologists.

Included in Dr. Sawyer's group were more than 500 scientists and engineers from various government agencies, universities, foundations, the Army and Navy. Their main job was to extract as much knowledge as possible from Operation Crossroads, including measurements of pressure, heat, light, nuclear radiations, electromagnetic propagation, radioactivity, optical radiation, and remote measurements of tidal data, shock, and the tracing of radioactivity.

Task Group 1.2, the Target Vessel Group, was under the command of Rear Adm. F. G. Fahrion, who also had the job of Commander of the Advance Echelon and Commander of all the Naval Task Groups until Admiral Blandy's arrival at Pearl Harbor. Directing all operations of the 93 target ships included the arrangements for getting them to Bikini Atoll and securely mooring them in the precise spot in the target complex.

Task Group 1.3, the Transport Group, was under the command of Capt. W. P. Davis, USN. This included the press ship USS *Appalachian,* and the two observer ships, USS *Blue Ridge* and USS *Panamint.* Eleven other transports quartered the crews after they had been evacuated from the target ships.

Task Group 1.4, the Army Ground Group, was a composite of units from the Signal Corps, Ordnance Department, Chemical Warfare Department, Quartermaster Corps, and Army Air Force, headed by Col. J. D. Frederick. Their principal task was to place many different kinds of Army equipment on board the ships for exposure to the blast and subsequent fallout.

Task Group 1.5, the Army Air Group, was commanded by Brig. Gen. R. M. Ramey. Its Air Transport Unit of ten C-54s provided logistic support, principally between the United States and Kwajalein. The Tactical Operations Unit, composed of thirteen B-29s, included the plane which dropped the bomb in Test A, and weather and radiological reconnaissance planes. Other air units in Task Group 1.5 provided photographic planes, instrument and communications planes, as well as press and observer flights.

The Drone Unit, achieving a "first" in aviation history, successfully operated six pilotless, radio-controlled, B-17 Flying Fortresses. During the bombing, they flew across the target area by radio guidance to bring back photographs and air samples through an atmosphere highly contaminated by radioactivity.

Task Group 1.6, the Navy Air Group, was commanded by Rear Adm. C. A. F. Sprague. They also attained a "first" in aviation history by perfecting radio-controlled drone planes, F6F Hellcats, which were catapulted from an aircraft carrier. After collecting air samples and taking photographs, the drones landed on Roi Island, Kwajalein Atoll. The Navy Air Group also operated four helicopters, fifteen PBM Mariner seaplanes, and several Avenger Torpedo

Bombers. The latter were used in guiding pilotless drone boats through the "hot" areas following the nuclear blasts.

Task Group 1.7, the Surface Patrol Group, was commanded by Capt. E. N. Parker, USN. It assumed the huge task of conducting the radiological safety operations following the world's first underwater detonation of the atomic bomb in Test B.

Task Group 1.8, the Service Group, was commanded by Capt. G. H. Lyttle, USN. Providing the many services of repair, fuel and water supply, mail, provisions, recreation, medical and evacuation, called for endless planning and resourcefulness. It was no small feat to keep 42,000 participants reasonably satisfied far out in an isolated part of the Pacific.

The magnitude of Operation Crossroads and all the component task groups can be appreciated by the statistics of men, ships, and miscellany involved—242 ships, 156 aircraft, four television transmitters, 750 cameras, 5,000 pressure gauges, 25,000 radiation recording devices, 204 goats, 200 pigs, 200 mice and 5,000 rats!

The very isolation of Bikini Atoll was one of the reasons for selecting that site for Operation Crossroads. Some of the other site requirements were: a protected anchorage at least six miles in diameter; a place that was virtually uninhabited; a location at least 300 miles from the nearest city and still within 1,000 miles of a B-29 base; clement weather; predictable winds directionally uniform at all altitudes from sea level to 60,000 feet; predictable water currents of great lateral and vertical dispersion; fast currents to carry radioactivity away from important fishing areas, shipping lanes and inhabited shores; and, finally, the area had to be under control of the United States. Bikini Atoll answered the problem of location in every respect, and had only 162 inhabitants.

Admiral Blandy selected May 15, 1946 as the target date for the first blast, with the underwater test to occur about six weeks later. However, a compromise in time was necessary. The postwar decline in funds and personnel called for an early date. Planning, particularly from the technical and scientific standpoint, required a longer time span before the first explosion. The time scale was changed on March 22, when President Truman ordered a delay of approximately six weeks in order to permit congressional observers a chance to complete legislative matters before the tests. Accordingly, the target date was set for July 1, 1946.

Considerable construction ashore had to be completed before the tests commenced. The 53rd Naval Construction Battalion accordingly set to work erecting twelve 75-foot steel towers for mounting cameras and other equipment, five 25-foot wooden towers, a dozen steel huts, five seismograph huts, photography beacons for obtaining fixes for aerial photography, recreation facilities for the thousands of military and civilian personnel, a water distillation system, seaplane ramp, camps, workshops, and dozens of other miscellaneous support installations.

Based on studies of the three previous atomic explosions—Alamogordo, Hiroshima and Nagasaki—the optimum altitude was selected for Test A. The only thing that could not be arranged in advance was the weather, but even that had to be predicted 24 hours in advance. A clear day with favorable winds was required, not only for good observation and photography, but also for accurately dropping the bomb from a high altitude.

The early morning prediction on June 30 was for favorable weather conditions, and the final preparations were made. Instruments were readied, the test animals were placed in their proper places, the target ships were closed, and the crews evacuated.

During the afternoon, the support ships began steaming southward toward the open sea. The deserted ships and lonesome beaches around the atoll were devoid of life except for the animals left blinking in the setting sun. The test animals were blissfully unaware that "doomsday" would come on the heels of the sunrise. The stage was set; the curtain was about to go up on the "biggest show on earth."

[31]

At 5:55 A.M. the following morning *Dave's Dream,* the B-29 carrying the atomic bomb for Test A, took off from Kwajalein. At bombing altitude, the plane arrived over Bikini Atoll. The crew proceeded to check wind velocity and fly through a "dress rehearsal" run. Maj. W. P. Swancutt, the plane commander, was not lacking for assistance or advice. In the B-29 were a brigadier general, two colonels, two other majors and four other officers of lesser rank. The weaponeers were Ens. D. L. Anderson and L. D. Smith.

USS *Nevada,* the center of the target, was marked with high-visibility paint and a flashing light. On the final run, the bomb bay doors were opened and the bombardier, Maj. H. H. Wood announced, "Bomb away, bomb away." The bomb ignited at 9 A.M. at the planned altitude, on the target date set, July 1. In milliseconds, a violent, uncontrolled nuclear chain reaction multiplied into a blinding flash which ripped the atmosphere apart. The energy instantaneously released was equal to 20,000 tons of TNT.

Dave's Dream made a 150-degree left turn and increased its getaway velocity. The F-13 photographic plane *Eggleston Eight* and *Dave's Dream* were the two nearest manned aircraft. Flying about twenty miles away were three Navy drone aircraft (converted F6Fs), and an Army B-17 drone. About thirty miles away, three more B-17 drones were aloft. On the surface ten to fifteen miles away were approximately fifteen of the principal support ships; others were scattered 15 to 25 miles away.

Observers watching the atomic explosion through specially designed goggles could not realize the full extent of the indescribably brilliant flash of light. The Icaroscope lenses worn admitted only .003 per cent of the light from the tremendous optical radiation released. The size and rapid expansion of the fireball was awesome. Energy from the splitting atoms ripped away from the center of the explosion with great velocity, emitting, along with optical radiation, a great pressure wave, nuclear radiation, and materials from the atomic device itself.

[32]

Near the center of the explosion the shock wave velocity was about 10,000 miles per hour. The hammer-blow quality of the shock wave slammed into every target ship within three to four miles of point zero. It continued as a violent wind, progressing concentrically outward, and dissipated into a pressure wave ten to twenty miles away.

The shock wave was followed closely by a large doughnut of fog called the condensation cloud. This cloud was formed by a suction wave racing closely behind the invisible shock wave. Because of the rarefied, cool air, the molecules of water vapor present condensed into countless billions of tiny droplets of white fog that was hemispherical in shape.

The white ball of fog expanded at the tremendous rate of thousands of miles per hour. The fog dome lasted only briefly because the trillion-watt fireball inside burned out its center. In about five seconds, the cloud formed into a huge white ring about two miles across. After two seconds of blinding brilliance, the fireball became obscured by the condensation cloud. Still expanding, it swept upward rapidly until the fireball again became obscured by the mushroom cloud which shot upward.

The well-known mushroom shape quickly rose to a spectacular height from the white-hot gases created by the intensity and magnitude of the fireball. At an altitude of five miles, the mushroom cloud was covered with the cap of tiny ice crystals buoyed by a stem of vapor, smoke, and a turbulent mixture of fission products.

Rising initially from the surface at 100 miles an hour, the cloud scooped up in its tail various gases created by ionizing radiations from the explosion. Individual molecules of nitrogen and oxygen collided to form molecules containing oxygen and nitrogen together. These molecules created an apricot color which beautifully tinted the huge "mushroom" of Test A. The fleecy beauty of this cloud was deceptive, for it was composed of deadly fission products. It became even more dangerous when it lost its characteristic mushroom shape and lingered in the area, indistinguishable from any other cloud.

Down below the mushroom, many scientific questions were answered that were directly connected with the future of the U.S. Navy at the threshold of the nuclear era. The fact that five ships sank during Test A is not too significant in itself, considering that twenty of the target ships were within a half mile of the blast center. Most of the ships carried ammunition and fuel, except in the upwind target sector. Here, burning fuel carried along the surface could envelop other test ships and destroy animals and instruments. Fire was a particularly serious threat because of the close disposition of the ships in relation to the nuclear blast.

The purpose of the explosion was to gather as much information as possible. Destroying the evidence with abnormal secondary effects, such as fire and exploding ammunition, would only deny information which was to be obtained at a high cost. Some of the unrealistic conditions during the tests were acknowledged beforehand and taken into consideration. The proximity of the anchored ships in the target area, and their inability to take evasive action, would not pertain in combat. Furthermore, commissioned ships would not be unmanned as were the test ships at Bikini. They were burning, flooding, and sinking, with no damage control measures taken to mitigate the destruction.

The first damage was caused by the intense heat of thermal radiation (which diminished rapidly as the fireball burned out), and gamma radiation (which drifted away as the great mushroom cloud ascended into the stratosphere). The thermal radiation caused burns on exposed test animals and damaged ships' topside equipment. However, it was the shock wave that hammered the ships' hulls and superstructures out of shape. Decks and hull plating were dished in, stacks smashed, masts bent, and exposed equipment torn from their foundations.

The B-17 drone planes gathered air samples at various altitudes over the blast area and flew back to Kwajalein for radiological study. The four TBM drones (former Grumman torpedo bombers) were launched from USS *Saidor* a few minutes after the detonation. They took valuable photographs of the sinking ships, since manned aircraft could not go into the area until four hours after the blast. The TBMs also assisted in controlling the drone boats, launched soon thereafter.

The drone boats picked up water samples and their geiger counters indicated the radiologically "hot" and "safe" areas. This enabled salvage parties to enter the lagoon to extinguish the flames still burning uncontrolled on several of the target ships.

By 2:30 P.M. Admiral Blandy announced that it was safe for the ships of Task Force One to reenter the lagoon, and his flagship USS *Mt. McKinley* led the way. Eighteen of the target ships were boarded before sundown to recover animals and scientific instruments for analysis. It took days before all could be recovered.

Diving and salvage operations proceeded as early as possible. The Japanese cruiser *Sakawa*, which had been ablaze for 24 hours, defied attempts to beach her by heeling over to port and sinking by the stern. The submarine *Skate*, with her outer hull virtually ripped from her exposed topside areas, was beached near Enyu Island.

As it turned out, the attack transport *Gilliam* was the closest ship to the blast, even though the battleship *Nevada* had been selected for this particular "honor." It was not calculated that a ship like the *Gilliam* could stand up under an atomic blast at close range. When divers went down to inspect her at the bottom of the lagoon, they proved these calculations absolutely correct. The ship's superstructure was smashed beyond recognition and her hull was little more than junk. Other nearby ships which caught the full fury of the blast and sank were the attack transport *Carlisle*, and two destroyers, *Anderson* and *Lamson*.

Curiously enough, the light aircraft carrier *Independence*, located about one third of a mile from the blast center, did not sink. Her damage, however, was spectacularly severe. Her port quarter, including part of the flight deck, was literally blasted off. The wooden deck planking was calculated to make perfect fuel for the thermal radiation of the fireball. It did. The extreme heat buckled the flight deck and broke it in several places. Her four stacks were gone and a fire in the hanger deck area added more damage after the shock wave. The metal hanger deck curtains were blown out, and exterior plating above the waterline was severely damaged.

The *Independence* was moved to a more accessible area for thorough inspection and recording of the damage. The inspection teams undertook the gigantic task of evaluating damage to thousands of compartments, spaces and installations. This information would be used by naval architects, engineers, ordnance experts, and damage control planners for years to come.

The overaged battleship *Arkansas*, within the one-half-mile radius of maximum destruction, sustained heavy damage. The once-proud ship was still burning in the early afternoon, the fires from her decks sending up billowing smoke. Practically all topside areas were bent out of shape, including superstructure, deckhouses, stanchions, doors and bulkheads. The battleships *New York* and *Pennsylvania* suffered comparatively light damage. However, the aircraft carrier *Saratoga*, nearby, was heavily damaged.

Strangely enough, the *Nevada*, the "bull's-eye" ship, suffered only moderately. Although the bomb did not explode directly over *Nevada*, she was only 1,500 to 2,000 feet away from the epicenter of the blast. Topmasts and yardarms gave way, her weather decks and bulkheads were bent, and thermal radiation had blackened painted surfaces topsides. Internally, there was virtually little evidence that she had been under an atomic explosion.

During the twenty-four days between Tests A and B, inspections and information gathering were completed, necessary repairs were made to damaged test ships, and they were rearranged in the target area. The center ship for the first underwater atomic explosion

(Test B), was *LSM-60*. The *Saratoga* and *Arkansas* were moored a little over 500 feet away, broadside to the center, in order to absorb the maximum damage from the blast. Twenty ships, large and small, were located within the half-mile radius of the underwater blast.

Six of the eight target submarines were placed in their fighting environment below the surface, since it was calculated that the greatest shock would be underwater. Test B would provide information for the construction of future submarines, and give an opportunity to study propagation of huge waves and underwater shock.

With ships, animals and instruments ready, the support ships began their withdrawal from the lagoon during the evening of July 24. Shortly after 6 A.M. the next morning, the last of the personnel departed, including Admiral Parsons, Dr. M. G. Holloway and R. S. Warner, Jr. Their job was to make final adjustments of the underwater nuclear device on board *LSM-60*.

The final moments of the countdown were heard by the 42,000 men of the task force, and by radio listeners around the globe. A fraction of a second before 8:35 A.M. Bikini time, July 25, 1946, the explosion detonated.

The brightly illuminated underwater fireball and gas bubble burst through the surface in a hundredth of a second, forming a huge dome. The fireball and a column of water shot upward, carrying with them the never-to-be-seen-again *LSM-60*—the first ship ever to be exploded into instant nothingness! As the water column raced skyward to a mile and a half in a minute, *LSM-60* was blasted into fine fragments and dust.

The head of the column flowered out to a mile and a half in diameter. It looked much like a huge cauliflower set on a stem about 2,000 feet wide. As the top of the "flower" reached its acme, thousands of side jets of water began to fall in a spectacular cascade, accelerating as they plunged back into Bikini lagoon.

Approximately ten million tons of water came booming back onto the surface, creating a base surge which appeared to be a roiling wave of water. It was actually spume, spray, and mist which formed a great circle like a smoke ring around the base of the column. It thickened as it traveled outward, ultimately reaching an altitude of 2,000 feet.

As the poisonous mist (loaded with fission products) settled, it contaminated most of the target ships with heavy radioactivity. When the mists cleared, the second man-made disaster of Operation Crossroads was examined.

The explosion, equivalent to 20,000 tons of TNT, had been converted instantaneously to shock wave and thermal, gamma, neutron, and various other nuclear radiations. Thermal and neutron radiation effects were almost entirely absorbed by the water. Lingering on long after the explosion were the radioactive wastes along with dangerous gamma radiation.

The severe shock wave did the initial damage. The incompressibility of water served as an excellent transmitter of the shock wave. Recorded at over 10,000 p.s.i. (pounds per square inch) at close range, and traveling at 3,500 miles per hour, the shock wave was gauged at thousands of p.s.i. at one-quarter to one-half mile away. The aerial photographs showed the quickly expanding circle of shock wave as it delivered almost a million tons of wallop to the hulls of the ships moored broadside to the shock center.

Nine ships went to the bottom. *Arkansas*, the closest of the target ships, suffered severe hull damage and sank before the spray had settled over the lagoon. *Saratoga*, the next closest ship, sank seven hours and forty minutes later. The explosion swept her decks clear of aircraft and other test materials. Her big, broad stack had crumpled to the flight deck, and her hull was badly ruptured. At 4:16 P.M. her superstructure sank below the surface.

The former Japanese battleship *Nagato* refused to cooperate with the post-mortems of Test B. Four and a half days after the blast, she slipped quietly and unnoticed under the surface at night, surprising everyone by her absence the following morning! Progressive flooding below the waterline finally took her down.

Of the four submerged submarines, three went to the bottom; *Pilotfish*, *Skipjack* and *Apogon*. The shock wave crushed hulls, ruptured plating, and dislocated internal machinery. Radioactive contamination continued for many weeks after the tests, and ships were later towed to Kwajalein, Pearl Harbor, and continental U. S. ports for further analysis.

As the support ships departed from Bikini, scientists and engineers carried with them facts which would help build better ships, afford protection against blast and radiation, and facts with which naval strategists would have to temper tactics and plans in the rougher, tougher, nuclear era ahead.

Through the years since 1946, the United States and her allies have set off over 200 atomic explosions. These explosions have been of various types, fired under a great variety of conditions. Basically, they are classified into five main types: 1) air burst (under 100,000 feet but high enough to keep the entire fireball above the surface); 2) high-altitude burst (above 100,000 feet); 3) underwater burst; 4) underground burst; and 5) surface burst (fireball touches land or water).

One very important development in nuclear testing was the ignition of the world's first thermonuclear blast, know as the hydrogen bomb. The first test shot took place on November 1, 1952, at Eniwetok Atoll. From that day on nuclear explosions jumped to a new magnitude of power. By March 1, 1954, a thermonuclear explosive was fired at Bikini; it was of such force that it equalled fifteen megatons.

The "old-fashioned" atomic explosives derived their power from a self-sustaining fission reaction which involved the splitting of the heaviest atoms—uranium 235 or plutonium 239. The explosion produced is measured in thousands of tons (kilotons) of TNT. The force of such an explosion produces heat equivalent to that of the sun (which produces temperatures in billions of degrees). This is the kind of heat (energy) required to trigger the fusion reaction of hydrogen in a thermonuclear explosion.

A thermonuclear explosion involves the fusion of two of the isotopes of hydrogen which forms one atom of helium, and in the process, releases one neutron. A tremendous amount of energy is released along with high-energy neutrons. The third part of this process (of three-explosions-in-one) occurs when these high-energy neutrons cause a third reaction by fissioning an outside layer of common, inexpensive uranium isotope U-238.

The end result is a successive fission-fusion-fission explosion of uranium-235, hydrogen (deuterium), and uranium-238. The explosive force of such a thermonuclear device is measured in terms of millions of tons (megatons) of TNT.

The first atomic bombs caused worldwide concern—and well they might. The destructive power of TNT was dwarfed by the power of the nuclear fission bombs. The hydrogen bomb, in turn, gave man a new magnitude of power with which to destroy himself. However, man cannot go backward scientifically—he must go forward. The scientific challenge is behind us. Ahead remains the challenge to use this newfound energy to serve man instead of to destroy him.

⚓

FOUR

Underway on Nuclear Power

THE BLACK silhouette of a unique submarine moved out into the channel of the Thames River and headed to sea for the first time. Painted on her sail was "571," the hull number of USS *Nautilus*— the world's first nuclear-powered submarine. It was the morning of January 17, 1955.

Before she moved away from her berth, the nuclear reactor was brought critical, a head of steam was built up, and *Nautilus* slowly slipped away from the shore. Once out in midstream, she headed downriver while many people, realizing the importance of the occasion, watched with great interest. Propelled by energy released from the atom, this was an important and exciting "first."

As *Nautilus* surged ahead for the open sea, her skipper, Comdr. Eugene P. Wilkinson, sent the historic message: "UNDERWAY ON NUCLEAR POWER."

In her wake, *Nautilus* left excited observers behind on the banks of the Thames. Upstream is the U. S. Naval Submarine Base, and downriver at Groton, Connecticut, is the Electric Boat Division of General Dynamics Corporation, where *Nautilus* had been built and launched. At her launching it was fitting that our first nuclear ship should be christened by our then first lady, Mrs. Dwight D. Eisenhower. *Nautilus* could not escape her destiny with greatness.

As she headed out into the Atlantic Ocean, *Nautilus* represented more than a century of striving toward a true submarine. She was the first submarine not dependent on the atmosphere to provide oxygen for her power plant. The diesel engines of previous sub-

[41]

marines required great quantities of air to operate and to recharge their electric storage batteries. Electric batteries give submarines a sporadic capability of propulsion submerged, but the faster the stored-up electric power is used, the sooner the batteries must be recharged. This requires surfacing for air in order to start the diesel engines for a recharge. Nuclear power permitted submarines to become completely free of the surface.

"Underway on nuclear power" was not a mere demonstration that a submarine could be propelled by nuclear fission. *Nautilus* dived off the coast of Connecticut and surged ahead all the way to San Juan, Puerto Rico, underneath the ocean waves. In the process, she set two world records—for sustained speed and for distance submerged.

It was only the beginning. *Nautilus* had put the atom to work with spectacular success. The nuclear-powered *Seawolf* and *Skate* were soon to follow with more "firsts" and more dramatic exploits in the depths of the oceans.

No less inspiring and dramatic was the energy of a slim, gray-haired gentleman who, with singleness of purpose, forced the nuclear program through to its fruition against all opposition. Drawing both barbs and admiration along the way, Adm. Hyman G. Rickover nevertheless accomplished a succession of brilliant engineering triumphs.

When Admiral Rickover was awarded the Enrico Fermi Award in November, 1964, he stated: "This award truly belongs to all the dedicated men and women in the laboratories, the factories, and in the shipyards who have worked so long and hard to develop our nuclear Navy. That we now have 51 atomic submarines in operation, and 41 more authorized by Congress, together with the nuclear-powered *Enterprise,* the cruiser *Long Beach,* and the frigate *Bainbridge,* is tribute to them."

Just as the age of flight gave man a new dimension in movement above the earth, so nuclear power gave him a new dimension in moving through the greatest wilderness on earth—the sea. The

United States had at last made a dramatic demonstration to the world that the atom could serve man as well as destroy him. Having shown its destructive force, nuclear energy now held the promise of turning the wheels of progress.

To better understand how our nuclear Navy functions, let us briefly review the basic process of how energy, from fissioning atoms, produces the power to drive nuclear ships through the water.

It was found that the atoms of uranium, the heaviest of our 92 known natural elements, could be split by bombardment with low-velocity neutrons. Being electrically neutral, neutrons, when released from within the nuclei of atoms, are free to fly out at random without being attracted by positively or negatively charged particles.

The nucleus of each atom is locked in by a powerful force of negatively charged electrons which whirl at great speed around the nucleus. Formed by neutrons, and positively charged protons, the nucleus exactly counterbalances the orbiting electrons, making each atom electrically neutral.

When a stray neutron is absorbed by a nucleus, it causes great agitation, resulting in the violent splitting of the nucleus into two approximately equal parts. These two parts weigh less than the original atom of uranium, and the difference in mass is partially converted into kinetic energy.

The atoms of any given element are not always identical. Some of the atoms of uranium, for example, are heavier than others. The various weights of any one element are called "isotopes." Some isotopes of uranium are easier to split than others.

The problem of producing nuclear energy would be much easier if common uranium were more accommodating. However, it is the rarer, lighter isotope of uranium (U-235) which splits when it absorbs a stray neutron. This lighter-weight isotope, U-235, is found in natural uranium in the ratio of one atom to every 140 of the heavier uranium isotopes (U-238). Separating these isotopes was described in Chapter II by the processes of thermal diffusion and electromagnetic separation.

In the explosive use of nuclear energy, the nuclei of U-235, or plutonium (P-239), explode in an uncontrolled nuclear reaction. This means that the fissionable mass goes through a chain reaction so fast that it explodes instantaneously with incredible force. However, in

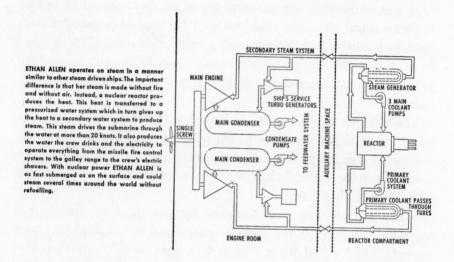

ETHAN ALLEN operates on steam in a manner similar to other steam driven ships. The important difference is that her steam is made without fire and without air. Instead, a nuclear reactor produces the heat. This heat is transferred to a pressurized water system which in turn gives up the heat to a secondary water system to produce steam. This steam drives the submarine through the water at more than 20 knots. It also produces the water the crew drinks and the electricity to operate everything from the missile fire control system to the galley range to the crew's electric shavers. With nuclear power ETHAN ALLEN is as fast submerged as on the surface and could steam several times around the world without refuelling.

a controlled chain reaction, the neutron bombardment and fission process taking place within a nuclear reactor can be started, brought to a desired temperature, sustained, and stopped whenever desired.

It takes only one neutron to cause fission of the nucleus of any one atom of U-235. This is an important fact in developing a self-sustaining chain reaction, because each fission releases an average of two and a half more neutrons. When these two or three neutrons burst out at a high rate of speed, they collide with other atoms of U-235, and again more neutrons are released to scatter at random.

This, in turn, causes the splitting of more nuclei. When enough fissionable material is assembled, a sustained nuclear chain reaction can be produced.

As the nuclei fly apart, the fission fragments collide with the surrounding material. The released neutrons may splat against structures within the reactor chamber, or they may be absorbed by other nuclei of the uranium fuel. Regardless of where the fission fragments scatter, the kinetic energy is converted directly into heat.

Within a nuclear reactor which has been "brought critical" (the fission reaction started), there are many billions of nuclei being split every second. The heat produced by myriad fissioning nuclei represents the usable energy from a nuclear reactor. This is only a small part of the energy released. The rest is dissipated in harmful radiations and other fission products which serve only to complicate the extraction of energy from nuclear fuels.

A nuclear reactor used in a ship's plant serves as an atomic furnace or fireroom. The fuel in the reactor is the mass of fissionable uranium called the reactor core. Nuclear fuel does not burn as do fossil fuels such as coal and oil, so there is no ignition of the fuel and no fire. The generation of heat is initiated by the production of neutrons, their absorption by nuclei of U-235, and their resultant fissioning.

In order to control the temperature within the nuclear reactor, it is necessary to establish a balance between the number of neutrons produced within the reactor and the neutrons which are absorbed. This control is effected by inserting and withdrawing control rods made of hafnium, or other neutron-absorbing material. When inserted fully, the control rods stop the fissioning reaction completely.

In the event of an emergency of any kind, the reactor is designed to "scram" automatically or manually. A "scram" is a quick stoppage of the nuclear fission process by immediately inserting the control rods to absorb the many released neutrons. This discontinues the nuclear chain reaction.

[45]

In controlling the reactor, it is very important to insure that no more heat is generated than can be carried away. Since extremely high temperatures are easily attainable, the big problem is not in generating heat but in removing it from the relatively small area of the reactor chamber. The nuclear reactors currently operating in the Fleet use pressurized water as the primary coolant to carry away the fission-produced heat.

The power plant of a nuclear submarine is divided into two systems, or loops: the primary (reactor) loop and the secondary (steam) loop. The two systems come in contact with each other only at the heat exchanger where steam is generated.

In the primary loop, the intense heat generated in the nuclear reactor is carried away by the coolant water which is circulated by pumps to the steam generator tubes. This is where the heat is transferred, or exchanged, to the steam-producing loop. The coolant water, which is under pressure so it cannot flash into steam, is pumped back to the reactor to absorb more heat and carry it away in a rapid, steady flow between the reactor and the heat exchanger. When the radioactive primary coolant water passes through the heat exchanger, it is sealed-in so that the steam is not contaminated in the essentially nonradioactive secondary loop.

The water in the steam loop is at a lower pressure than in the primary system, so it boils when heated and bursts into steam. From the boiler, steam passes through a steam drum to remove excess moisture before the pressure forces the steam into the blades of the turbo-generators. These turbines provide the submarine with power for main propulsion and auxiliary purposes.

Continuing on its way, the remaining steam enters the condenser. Here it is condensed to water and again pumped back through the steam generator tubes of the heat exchanger to make more steam for the whirling turbines.

A great amount of power is required in a submarine to energize the ship's electronic and electrical equipment—not to mention the coffee pot and the electric shavers! While under way, all the equipment on board is powered indirectly by fissioning atoms, from the sonar console to the juke box.

Not all of the energy released by fissioning atoms is usable energy. The radiation which produces fission waste products, presents a continuous hazard. The reactor therefore is surrounded by water shielding and by a thick layer of lead and polyethylene to protect the ship's company from radiation effects.

When a reactor is operating in a nuclear submarine, no one is permitted to enter the lower level of the reactor compartment. The upper level of the compartment is a shielded space to permit safe access of the officers and crew over the reactor area, when passing to and from the after spaces of the submarine.

There is no chance of a runaway reactor causing a nuclear explosion such as might be expected from a nuclear weapon. The heat would get out of control and an explosion might result which would be more in the order of a conventional chemical explosion. If such a thing did happen, the big problem would be the possibility of radioactive contamination. This points up the relatively high cost of nuclear propulsion design, for much shielding and many safety and monitoring devices have to be provided.

Much of the care, quality control, and selection of materials in nuclear design and engineering are devoted to reliability and avoiding radiation problems. Solving these problems is well worth the effort, because the nuclear power plant provides a propulsion system with a unique departure—at no time in the cycle of the primary or secondary loop is there any demand for oxygen. It is a closed-cycle power system which makes it possible for a nuclear-powered submarine to operate submerged for months at a time without surfacing.

Achieving the goal of operable nuclear submarines was an uphill struggle. After we had learned to make nuclear explosives, we were still a long way from nuclear propulsion. With the first promise of a sustained fission reaction in 1939, the Navy was intrigued with the possibilities of nuclear power for ships, particularly for submarines. The dust of World War II had hardly settled when the Navy again directed its attention to the exciting possibilities of this non-destructive application of atomic energy.

Unfortunately, atomic energy emerged from the war under a veil of secrecy and tight control by the Manhattan District. Information concerning the nature of work going on in their laboratories was not initially made available to Navy scientists. This successfully served to stymie any immediate ideas of launching a full-fledged nuclear propulsion program.

There were other obstacles, too. The Navy did not know what the national policy would be concerning the control of atomic energy. There was a possibility that a research program, once started, would be wiped out by either control policy or by duplication of effort within the Manhattan District. Until these things were determined, there was little basis upon which to authorize funds.

Fortunately, the Navy put in an early bid for consideration for nuclear propulsion. In August, 1944, Gen. Leslie R. Groves, head of the Manhattan District, created the National Defense Research Committee, to make recommendations for a postwar policy on the development of atomic energy. Dr. R. C. Tolman was appointed Vice Chairman, and Rear Adm. Earle W. Mills, then Assistant Chief of the Bureau of Ships, was the military representative.

Members of the committee visited the Naval Research Laboratory in November, 1944, where they interviewed Rear Adm. A. H. Van Keuren, Director of NRL, Dr. Gunn, and Dr. Abelson. During this meeting, the need for nuclear-propelled submarines was presented. Sufficiently impressed by the discussions at NRL, the Tolman Committee recommended in its final report of December, 1944, that research and development studies be urgently pursued to develop nuclear power for propulsion of naval ships, particularly for submarines.

In late 1945, Admiral Mills arranged a conference with General

Groves and Navy officials to investigate the possibilities of nuclear propulsion. The biggest handicap pointed out by General Groves was the limited amount of fissionable material. He also invoked the Presidential directive of August, 1945, which restricted the release of information related to the atomic bomb. This was the reason for his reluctance to share nuclear energy information with Navy personnel. Clearance was not granted unless they were assigned full-time to the Manhattan District.

It is interesting to note that at this same time the Soviet Union was at least as well informed about the progress of the Manhattan District as were the naval proponents of nuclear propulsion—thanks to the traitorous espionage of Klaus Fuchs.

On March 14, 1946, Secretary of the Navy James Forrestal sent a letter to Secretary of War Patterson stating the Navy's desire to commence a program for the development of atomic power for ship propulsion. The reply proposed that Navy personnel be assigned to the Manhattan District to work on the Daniels Power Pile. This was an experimental project to develop a small stationary power plant for the production of electric power. Since this project was not aimed toward ship propulsion, the Navy was not overly enthusiastic about it. At least it was a "foot in the door," and the Bureau of Ships sent a small team of technical representatives. Through the latter part of 1946 and most of 1947, this Navy group worked on the project at the laboratories at Oak Ridge.

The Atomic Energy Commission, which had taken over atomic energy matters from the Manhattan District on January 1, 1947, halted further work on this type of power pile reactor pending a survey of alternate methods. However, the experience gained by the Navy technicians was not lost. Headed by Vice Admiral Rickover, then a captain, they formed the nucleus of the tremendous Navy effort toward developing the first nuclear-powered submarine.

At Oak Ridge, they requested further study of a high-pressure, water-cooled reactor for a submarine, an idea first proposed there

[49]

by Dr. A. M. Weinberg. The water-cooled type of reactor eventually propelled the first nuclear submarine, USS *Nautilus*.

The going was by no means easy for the Rickover group. By the end of 1947, the AEC had not assigned a formal project for ship propulsion, and a shortage of funding and technical personnel did not help. Captain Rickover reported that the AEC was then primarily interested in producing fissionable material for bombs, and other nuclear power projects were only secondary.

Since there was little incentive for the electric power industry to invest in the development of atomic power, he suggested that the drive to develop nuclear propulsion for naval ships must come from the Navy itself. He especially urged the development of atomic power for submarines, pointing out that the scientific problems were solved and the way was clear for the engineering phase of the program.

Vice Admiral Mills, who became Chief of the Bureau of Ships, appointed Captain Rickover as a special assistant, and gave him the big job of obtaining high-level Navy and Department of Defense authorization for developing and building a nuclear-powered submarine. On January 20, 1948, Admiral Mills sent a proposal to the AEC giving details on the design and construction of a nuclear power plant. Included was a request for training more people and expanding the studies then in progress, particularly for extensive work on radiation shielding, materials, and heat-transfer systems.

The Research and Development Board, headed by Dr. Vannevar Bush, sent a favorable endorsement to the Secretary of Defense. The report stated that construction of the nuclear-powered submarine was technically feasible, and that there was an urgent strategic need for them. It also recommended that the AEC establish a formal project for the submarine and assign a priority for the work.

On April 27, the AEC authorized the Submarine Thermal Reactor (STR) project. After its long battle against red tape, disinterest, and meager support, this marked a Navy victory. Even Dr.

Underway on Nuclear Power

J. R. Oppenheimer, head of the General Advisory Committee, considered the project as technically premature. Against this kind of opposition it was clear that solving the engineering problems posed only a part of the up-hill struggle toward developing the Navy's first nuclear reactor.

An AEC contract made with the Westinghouse Electric Company on June 28, 1948, called for designing and developing a power conversion system for a naval ship, using high-pressure water as the medium for heat transfer. The AEC executed another contract with Westinghouse on December 10, 1948, to develop the design and construction of the STR Mark I reactor—a land-based prototype plant—and the STR Mark II. The latter was to be the shipboard power plant that would be installed in USS *Nautilus*.

The Argonne National Laboratory of the AEC, using many of the group that had worked on the Daniels Power Pile, proceeded with the research and conceptual design. To further the work, land was purchased near Pittsburgh where the AEC built the Bettis Laboratory.

The time scale for the first nuclear-powered submarine was set by the Chief of Naval Operations in August, 1949, to be ready for operational evaluation in 1955. The Chief of the Bureau of Ships refined this time goal, stating that the submarine should be ready to get underway from the shipyard, complete with nuclear power plant, by January, 1955. The award of contract for construction of the first nuclear submarine went to the Electric Boat Division of General Dynamics Corporation at Groton, Connecticut in August, 1951. Her keel was laid on the following June.

In August, 1950, construction was started on the STR Mark I nuclear plant at the National Reactor Test Station, out in the desert at Arco, Idaho. Work progressed simultaneously on the Mark I and Mark II reactors during 1951 and 1952. As technology advanced, many improvements were incorporated in the Mark II reactor. To support the new nuclear technology, a program commenced to train

[51]

scientists, engineers, and technicians in the art of working with the new techniques, instruments, and materials.

By the end of March, 1953, the Mark I reactor at Arco was first made to go critical. Two months later, the mock-up submarine operated on its first power run. It is paradoxical that the first test of this source of propelling submarines through the water should be made in a remote desert area so far from the Atlantic or Pacific Oceans. In June, the "submarine" made a simulated "submerged crossing" of the Atlantic Ocean. Instead of actual propellers driving a real submarine, the power generated was dissipated by a paddle-wheel turning through a tank of water. It should not escape posterity to note that this was the first time in history that nuclear energy had turned a wheel!

Nautilus was launched on January 21, 1954, and commissioned on September 30. Thus, the target date to be ready for sea in January was realized. This brings us to the morning of January 17, 1955, when *Nautilus* first got under way.

That day was a day of triumph for the Navy, for the many people whose talents and labors produced the final product, and for the United States, whose international prestige and respect now reached a high peak. However, the one man above all others who could take tremendous satisfaction in the achievement was Admiral Rickover. He and his hard-working team had produced, in a few years of inspired effort, what some experts on nuclear energy thought would take twenty-five years.

The date was Saturday, April 11, 1959. The place was the ward-room of the nuclear-powered USS *Skipjack*, under way at sea—a peculiar, though appropriate, place for the Joint (Congressional) Committee on Atomic Energy to meet. The chairman of the Committee, Senator Clinton P. Anderson, was addressing the group, while the submarine cruised submerged off the Atlantic Coast:

"It was four years ago last month, on March 20, 1955, that the

Joint Committee held a meeting aboard USS *Nautilus,* the world's first nuclear submarine. Congressmen Chet Holifield and James Van Zandt, and Senator Pastore, who are present here today, were among those who were with me that memorable day four years ago aboard what was then the only nuclear submarine at sea. Since then, five additional nuclear submarines have gone to sea: the *Seawolf, Skate, Swordfish, Sargo,* and the *Skipjack.* This is a marvelous record of the accomplishments of Admiral Rickover and his splendid team."

During the deliberations of the Committee, Admiral Rickover made an announcement:

"The captain of the *Skipjack* has just reported to me that we are at . . . . the greatest depth a submarine has ever been, and that we have attained . . . . the highest speed any submarine has ever attained. This is the first congressional committee that has deliberated so deeply and so fast."

Although his sense of humor is not as well-known as his achievements, Admiral Rickover, at the same committee meeting in *Skipjack,* shared credit with the many devoted people who had made nuclear submarines possible. In so doing, his words aptly summarize the story of this chapter:

"There is hardly a single idea that is new. What really counts is to take an idea, fight for the authority to do it, establish the organization, find and train the necessary scientists and engineers, justify to Congress the large sums of money involved, worry over and solve the thousands of technical difficulties. Well, about two hundred million dollars and eight years after the 1946 'idea,' and with the devoted efforts of many, many hundreds of scientists and engineers, and the participation of many hundreds of companies, we finally had the *Nautilus.*"

The historic message sent by Commander Wilkinson from USS *Nautilus* in 1955 has been a prophecy and fulfillment. For since that time the U. S. Navy has, in ever-increasing tempo, been "underway on nuclear power."

[53]

FIVE

New Horizons

THE UNDERSEA world of the nuclear submarine is a world without visible horizons. Its domain is the deep, eternal darkness of the oceans which cover almost three-quarters of the globe. However, the new horizons for nuclear submarines are those of achievement which appear to be as infinite as the horizons of the seas.

During her first two years of operation, *Nautilus* established a number of speed and endurance records. On her first nuclear core, she steamed over 62,000 nautical miles without refueling. This is approximately the mileage that a conventional submarine would get from two million gallons of diesel oil. In terms of bulk, the handful of uranium fuel provides the same power as a line of railroad tank cars over a mile and a half long! The second nuclear core was vastly improved, and the third was capable of steaming twice as far, at a cost of twenty percent less than the first. The life of a nuclear core is now measured not in miles, but in years of operation.

Speed and endurance submerged do not tell the entire story of the new family of nuclear submarines. They can now go where submarines could not venture before. *Nautilus* demonstrated this new capability in a most dramatic way when Comdr. William R. Anderson, and the ship's company, blazed a new submarine trail under the polar ice from the Pacific to the Atlantic.

Nautilus cast off from the submarine base at Pearl Harbor on July 23, 1958, and steamed nonstop to Portsmouth, England, arriving on August 12. En route she steamed 8,146 nautical miles, including 1,830 miles under the North Polar ice cap. With the prolonged submergence required, it would have been impossible to undertake this trip without nuclear power. The historical cruise opened up a new underwater sea route over the top of the world, and a vast sea area for submarine operations which had hitherto been a virtually inaccessible waste area.

For a conventionally powered submarine to surface through a layer of ice thirty to forty feet thick would be quite impossible. A nuclear submarine can wait until a polynya in the ice is found and then punch its way through the relatively thin ice.

The art of bringing a submarine up through the polar ice was developed by Comdr. James Calvert, skipper of the USS *Skate*. Her first cruise under the ice pack was in August, 1958, ten days after the *Nautilus'* voyage. Calvert attained the North Pole from an east to west direction, and was thus the first to circumnavigate the globe in one hour! It was by traveling in a circle just one mile from the Pole that the *Skate* established this new global speed record.

Capt. Richard B. Laning, skipper of the second nuclear submarine USS *Seawolf*, set a record for sustained submergence. Diving in the Atlantic in August, 1958, *Seawolf* surfaced on October 6, sixty days later. This was a test for both men and equipment which furthered nuclear submarine endurance under the sea.

The first nuclear submarine excursions under the polar ice, though bold and progressive, were of relatively moderate duration. On March 15, 1959, Calvert again took *Skate,* our third nuclear submarine, under the polar ice, where she steamed for 3,090 nautical miles continuously in twelve days. This demonstrated that our nuclear submarines could operate in the Arctic as long as they wanted to remain. The full value of this ability was realized later with the advent of the Polaris submarines.

Another significant facet of the huge operating area under the polar ice is the virtual elimination of all of the submarines' traditional surface and air enemies. Only one possible enemy remains under the ice: another nuclear-powered submarine.

On January 18, 1960, the USS *Sargo,* skippered by Lt. Comdr. John H. Nicholson, departed from tropical Hawaii and steamed toward the winter night of the Arctic. She was to advance the art of global submarining still another step. Previous transpolar submarine voyages had been made during seasons when the polar ice was not at its worst. *Sargo* set out to demonstrate that nuclear submarines could negotiate the rugged, frozen trail across the top of the world through the winter ice.

The jagged peaks of ice reaching down from above were recorded by *Sargo* during her ice-bound cruise. Cruising under the ice for thirty-one days and 6,000 miles, she smashed through twenty times. On sixteen of these surfacings, she crunched through ice as thick as three feet.

The *Sargo* cruise showed how rugged our nuclear submarines were, and where they needed "ruggedizing," if vulnerable design features were detected. As a gesture, Hawaii's state flag was planted at the North Pole, and after the five-and-a-half-week cruise, *Sargo* returned to Pearl Harbor, ice-battered but triumphant.

Improvements in the nuclear power plant of our modern submarines are only a part of the story of the United States' new family of modern submarines. An experimental hull shape was developed at the Navy's David Taylor Model Basin, located along the Potomac upriver from Washington, D. C. It was a blimp-shaped submarine hull which was first used in the USS *Albacore,* an experimental diesel-electric submarine. The speed and maneuverability performance of this submarine were so exciting that an entirely new generation of nuclear submarines was produced.

The first "marriage" of nuclear power with the high-speed *Albacore* hull was in the USS *Skipjack.* This submarine and others of her class were an unqualified success. Commanded by Comdr. William W. Behrens, *Skipjack* exceeded the speed and depth of any previous submarine on April 11, 1959. Turning and banking like an airplane, her performance was both spectacular and exciting. Since the full capabilities of these attack submarines is classified material, neither her speed nor depth attained can be revealed. However, of one thing we can be sure, whatever records were established by *Skipjack,* they have since been exceeded many times.

One very important point concerning the performance records of nuclear submarines should be emphasized. They are not set merely for the record, for a silver plaque or some other trophy. Each new step in performance is aimed toward increasing the nuclear submarines' operational effectiveness and widening the scope of their mission spectrum for America's defense.

Admiral Rickover, in a recent speech before the Joint Committee on Atomic Energy, stated: "Each one of these nuclear submarines constitutes a complete task force in itself. Each of these ships is able, on its own, to perform functions which outstrip the requirements placed on it. In a large surface-ship task force, the Navy makes a tremendous investment to get a self-sufficient offensive capability where and when it wants it, with a capability for staying there and doing a job. Now in the nuclear submarine we have such a capability at low cost. The ocean acts as its armor. As a result, the submarine can be made all weapon, rather than part weapon and part shield. Therefore, we should look at each new improved feature which is added to the submarine as an increase in the effectiveness of this one-ship task force."

On November 10, 1959, a 447-foot submarine, the largest then existent in the world, was commissioned at Groton, Connecticut. Unique in size and design, she is listed in the Navy registry as USS *Triton* (SSN 586). The power from her twin reactors, her hull configuration, and much greater reserve buoyancy, give her versatility in operating with a surface task force as well as submerged operations.

The Commanding Officer of *Triton,* Capt. Edward L. Beach, was ordered to Washington for an important conference on February 4, 1960. Here he learned that *Triton* was chosen to make a submerged circumnavigation of the world! She was apparently selected on the basis of her size, speed, and the added dependability of her two-reactor power plant.

The purposes of the round-the-world cruise under the sea were for "geophysical and oceanographic research and to determine the habitability, endurance and psychological stress (all extremely important to the Polaris program) . . . the voyage should be made entirely submerged, undetected by our own or other forces, and completed as soon as possible."

Triton got underway from New London, Connecticut on February 16, 1960, and headed for the St. Peter and St. Paul Rocks about 3,400 nautical miles away, fifty-five miles north of the equator off the coast of Brazil. This marked the point of departure and point of return for the complete submerged circumnavigation of the world.

The only planned contact with the surface was coming up to periscope depth to take sightings for celestial navigation when the sun, moon or stars were visible. The time-honored plotting of position by celestial navigation was used during the voyage to check on the behavior of a then-new and complicated machine called the Ships' Inertial Navigation System (SINS). It automatically calculates latitude and longitude by use of sensitive and precise gyroscopes. *Triton* also used the brief periods at periscope depth to pump fresh air through the ship because the oxygen generating system was not then developed for nuclear submarines.

On February 24, *Triton* departed from St. Peter and St. Paul Rocks and began her world-encircling cruise, following the approximate route that Ferdinand Magellan had sailed 438 years before! The submarine steamed around Cape Horn, South America; across the Pacific through the Philippines; around the Cape of Good Hope, South Africa; and back to St. Peter and St. Paul Rocks. The colorful cruise reached a complete cycle when *Triton* sighted the "Rocks" at 1330 on April 25, 1960—60 days, 21 hours, and 26,723 nautical miles later. Ferdinand Magellan's ship *Vittoria,* after three years of sailing, returned to Seville, Spain on September 8, 1522, in one of the world's most dramatic historical parallels!

From the "Rocks," *Triton* set course for Tenerife, Canary Islands —Magellan's point of departure from Europe before setting out on his world cruise. The rendezvous point off Cádiz, Spain, brought *Triton* within 3,000 nautical miles of home—the longest miles of the voyage for the crew. When she surfaced off Rehoboth, Delaware on May 10, she had been submerged for eighty-four days and had logged 36,014 nautical miles.

Upon returning to New London, *Triton* had demonstrated that a nuclear submarine was able to perform any global mission required; the voyage had also added greatly to our fund of knowledge on oceanography and submerged navigation.

In general, we had advanced in three areas of submarining: in knowledge of nuclear submarines and their capabilities; in experience concerning the endurance and stamina of the men who must go down into the sea in nuclear ships; and in knowledge of the sea environment in which nuclear submarines can and must operate for prolonged cruises without surfacing.

On August 1, 1960, another nuclear submarine, the USS *Seadragon,* skippered by Comdr. George P. Steele, headed northward from Portsmouth, New Hampshire in quest of new horizons. She was destined to carve a new route to the Pole by way of a northwest passage through a series of sounds and straits in northern Canada. En route, *Seadragon* had a rendezvous with the mountainous icebergs of Baffin Bay.

Encounters with icebergs had previously been avoided by ships of all types. Collisions in the past had proved the great hazards presented by these drifting ice monsters—the *Titanic* disaster was without question the most dramatic of all. Steaming directly underneath one of these bluish-white icebergs, *Seadragon* marked a first in history. She had to dive more than 300 feet to get under a huge iceberg 879 feet wide and 1,471 feet long! Scientific data on this armada of glacial giants was gathered in the hope that it would make the seas safer through a better understanding of these frozen phenomena.

On the lighter side, the ship's company conducted a sports experiment at the North Pole—baseball was played there for the first time. If any errors were made during the entire cruise, they were all committed during this game. Playing in weather twenty-eight degrees below zero and hampered by heavy clothing, championship baseball could hardly be expected! With the pitcher's box at the Pole, a home run would take the base runner around the world—from today into tomorrow and back again! Sliding into first base on the ice meant a long walk back from right field. The game was not recorded in scientific annals, but it proved one interesting thing—beer on ice may be here to stay, but baseball is not!

Seadragon completed her polar voyage after 8,800 eventful miles when she steamed into Pearl Harbor on September 14, 1960. Greeting her at her new home port were Navy officials, dignitaries, and—best of all—the newly transplanted families. All were duly proud of the first submarine to have made the transpolar voyage from the Atlantic to the Pacific.

The operational accomplishments of our nuclear submarines follow on the heels of technological advances—higher speeds, quieter running, and pressure hulls which permit even deeper operations under the sea. Therefore, the *Thresher*-class submarines included improvements over the *Skipjack* class.

Submerging to greater depths creates new problems which must be solved. As a submarine dives, it is exposed to tremendous pressures which increase about forty-four pounds per square inch for each one hundred feet of depth. The packing boxes around the propeller shafts, the piping, and the joints exposed to these high pressures must be stronger and free of structural weaknesses. With 3,000 or more joints built into the piping of a submarine, the quality control becomes an enormous job. In very many cases, the rigid standards of quality material and workmanship required by Admiral Rickover have set new and unprecedented standards among the hundreds of contractors and subcontractors involved in the construction and manufacture of nuclear submarines.

One fundamental method of eliminating thousands of complicated parts, piping, gauges, controls, and instruments is improvement through more simplified design. Potential trouble areas can then be eliminated. One of the promising areas of design simplification is a new type of nuclear reactor. Not only does it have fewer working parts, it also promises to provide nuclear submarines with quieter operation.

Great advances in maneuverability and controls for submarines is another area where our technology is stepping ahead. A system is being developed called the Fast Reaction Integrated Submarine Control (FRISCO)—an automatic reaction type of submarine control and safety system. Instead of diving planes at the bow and stern, wing-like sail planes now protrude from either side of the superstructure for better control of the blimp-like, high-speed submarine hulls. Single propellers have also contributed toward greater maneuverability for our nuclear attack submarines.

The submarines of World War II were designed for surface running with a superstructure deck, guns, lifelines, and other cluttered topside fittings, which offered great water resistance when running submerged. Nevertheless, they did a devastating job against the enemy. These diesel-electric submarines sank more than five million tons of enemy shipping during the war. The loss of fifty-two U. S. submarines and more than 3,500 officers and men was the sacrifice made in return. If they had been nuclear-powered submarines, it is probable that over 90 per cent of these submariners would have survived the war. Offensively, the faster surface ships which disappeared over the horizon carrying enemy troops, arms, and material might never have arrived to fight in the island-hopping war of the Pacific if they had been opposed by nuclear submarines.

For conventionally powered submarines, the price of submerged speed was costly in terms of stored power from their batteries. Cruising at high speed when submerged vastly shortened their ability to remain below. Furthermore, surfacing meant loss of concealment while often facing an enemy with superior gunfire, speed, and maneuverability. Nuclear submarines are freed of this danger in warfare because they can travel at higher speeds almost indefinitely, and their endurance far outlasts that of conventionally powered surface ships. *Nautilus* and all subsequent nuclear submarines can go faster than twenty knots (an ultra-conservative statement), and sustain speed as long as needed.

Along with the twentieth century came the conquest of the greatest unexplored frontier on earth—the seas. Before 1900, the ocean depths had little effect on world history. The submarines of both world wars started a "rock-slide" of historical events during the first half of the century, and the nuclear submarine has turned this "rock-slide" into an avalanche of achievement.

The new horizons under the sea are infinite, and many of the explorers in this salt-water infinity will sail in nuclear submarines. In peace and in war, our submariners must explore the canyons, plains, and mountains below until they become as familiar as the geographical landmarks rising above the sea. It has already been demonstrated that they are the Magellans of the future.

SIX

Training Our Nuclear Navy Men

ON THE East Coast, the West Coast, and the Gulf of Mexico, submarines are sliding down the building ways in an unprecedented number. New submarine hulls are splashing into the water in frequent launching ceremonies. With each splash, 100 to 130 well-qualified officers and men must be ready to step on board.

Where they come from and how they get there is the story of training our nuclear Navy men. Matching flesh and blood with atoms and steel is a challenge as dramatic as the manpower buildup during World War II. However, there are important differences in the buildup for our nuclear Navy. All of the men in the nuclear program must be volunteers, specially selected and qualified through intensive training.

One would think that the burgeoning submarine program in the Navy would exact a compromise in quality of personnel as the quantity increased. Yet, one of the real eye-openers in our nuclear program is the uniformly high quality maintained in selecting and training the men in the first through the fiftieth nuclear ship—ad infinitum. What is more important is the proof that the United States can still provide an almost inexhaustible number of high quality young men to fill important assignments.

Given an opportunity to excell and improve, every man on board works toward advancement in rating. A high percentage of the crews in Polaris submarines advance to officer rank—far above the Navy's overall average.

In Groton, Comdr. C. D. Grojean, a skipper of the *Thomas A.*

Edison, said: "I believe the high standards demanded by Admiral Rickover have permeated through our submarine crews right down to the youngest seaman on board. I am amazed at the technical competence of our sailors in maintaining and repairing complicated equipment."

When Comdr. William R. Anderson returned from the first voyage under the North Polar ice pack, he was sure that *Nautilus* had the finest crew ever assembled. Captains Richard B. Laning and James Calvert, skippers of the *Seawolf* and *Skate* respectively, were equally convinced that their crews were the best. It seems that every commanding officer of a nuclear submarine believes his particular crew is unbeatable.

Following the booming success of *Nautilus,* the submarine program has gained momentum steadily. In the ten years since 1954, over fifty nuclear submarines have joined the fleet, and twenty-eight are of the large Polaris type, requiring two complete crews instead of one. Our nuclear armada of submarines and surface ships has siphoned off a tremendous supply of choice manpower to operate nuclear power plants, handle nuclear weapons, and operate the instrumentation associated with them.

Most of the nuclear-trained men are absorbed into the Polaris program, since Polaris submarines will continue to have the highest construction priority for several years. Ten thousand men are required in a two- or three-year period. During the 1964 school year at New London/Groton, FBM Team Training was completed for twenty Polaris submarines, totalling forty crews.

When the word crackles over the PA system to "Man Battle Stations, Missile," many feet start pounding along the decks of a Polaris submarine. Its sets in motion over 120 men and a dozen officers, representing hundreds of years of training and experience. They are the cream of the crop, and work hard after being selected for the Polaris program.

In order to become a Polarisman, you must be a submariner first, and this in itself is no easy achievement. Initially, a large percentage of Polarismen were in the submarine program. However, the rapid expansion of our Polaris fleet required an additional source of manpower. To attract good men, the Navy offered high school graduates who could pass the rigid tests a chance to enter the Polaris or Nuclear Seaman Recruit Program.

Three basic programs leading to Polaris duty are: the regular submarine school program, the nuclear power program, and the Polaris program. Tracing a man's career from mufti to Polaris submarine might typically follow the pattern of: Recruit Training, Basic (Class "A") Trade School, Submarine School, Polaris Training, and assignment to an FBM submarine.

If he prefers the missile program rather than the nuclear power program, he has a choice of four ratings. In the electronics phase of the Polaris program, he may elect a school for Electronics Technician, Fire Control Technician, or Missile Technician. In the launcher field, he must first learn the art of the Torpedoman before additional training on the Polaris missile.

To become an Electronics Technician, a man must complete a thirty-eight week course at Great Lakes or San Francisco. The Fire Control Technician rating requires twenty-four weeks of study at Great Lakes, San Diego, or Bainbridge, Maryland. Torpedoman's Mates, after an eleven-week course at Key West or San Diego, may continue for another twenty-two week course at Dam Neck, Virginia, to become Missile Technicians.

Following his class "A" school, the aspiring Polarisman begins eight weeks of classes in the Submarine School to learn the rudiments of submarine life and escape training techniques. Basic submarine training schools are of particular interest because they are the gateway through which most of our nuclear Navy men pass. Schooling is divided between study and operating the equipment, both ashore and in an actual submarine.

During the fiscal year 1964, 391 students graduated from the

Officer Basic Submarine Course, and 6,782 graduated from the Enlisted Basic Submarine Course at New London/Groton, Connecticut. Because of the teamwork required, students must learn about the entire submarine; its power plant, controls, buoyancy tanks, weapons, and operating procedures. In every phase of study, his learning is supplemented by working with others in underway training.

All submariners must learn the techniques of escape through the water in the event a submarine is disabled on the bottom. The free ascent method is taught in a tall training tank. With his lungs full of air, a trainee steps into the water at a selected depth through an air lock. As he ascends, he slowly exhales to neutralize the pressure on his lungs. All students are trained to ascend from a fifty-foot depth using this method of emergency escape.

Training the men in the use of controls for diving and surfacing is begun on the Askania trainer, a dry-land mock-up simulating the tilting attitude of a submarine. Students then advance to the Universal Submarine Simulator. A newer device, it approximates the motion of the higher-speed attack submarines of the *Skipjack* class. When they take hold of the controls of a real submarine, they are familiar with the "feel of the wheel."

A student does not become a full-fledged submariner upon graduating from Submarine School. After approximately nine months of actual service in a submarine, a crewman may finally qualify to wear his twin-dolphin pins. This mark of distinction tells the world that he is a qualified submariner, that he can trace the myriad pipes and cables, know where they go, what each system does, and how it works. To those of us who are mystified by the jumble of assorted hardware under the hood of the family automobile, it evokes an extra measure of respect.

The Blue-and-Gold two-crew system used in Polaris submarines created a very busy FBM Training Department at the Submarine School in New London/Groton. Here, refresher courses are offered in the Polaris Weapons and Navigation Systems. Maintenance refresher training is given for the off-crews, and team training for all new crews. Some of the sophisticated training equipment includes elaborate simulation of the FBM subsystems, using electronic digital and analog computers.

An A-1 Polaris training missile is used to enable off-crew practice in casualty analysis, maintenance procedures, missile firing, submerged navigation, and ship control. For those who work in the nuclear power plant, courses are given to provide maintenance refresher training on nuclear propulsion and auxiliary equipment. No one is allowed to get "rusty." The high level of training is one reason for Polaris crews proving so self-sufficient and adept at underway maintenance and repair.

Every time an advanced missile, a component or a control panel is brought into the fleet, more training is required by Polaris operators. Much of the training on new or improved equipment can be accomplished during the on-shore period between patrols. However, if such training is too extensive, it requires assignment to an advanced school. Most of the Polarismen do attend advanced schools after they have served for some time in a submarine.

The ratings selected for training in nuclear propulsion are Machinist's Mate, Electrician's Mate, or Electronics Technician. Early in the nuclear program other ratings were included. Before going to Nuclear Power School, the volunteer with a high school diploma must be a U. S. citizen with "secret" clearance, recommended by his commanding officer, and be able to pass written tests.

The Navy's Nuclear Power Program requires a full year of training for officers and enlisted men for duty in submarines as well as surface ships. The high level of competence demanded calls for extensive study in nuclear-power plant theory and operation. Divided into these two parts, the training program is accomplished through collaboration between the Navy, the Atomic Energy Commission, and industry.

The first part is a six-month course in science and technology, at

Bainbridge, Maryland or Mare Island, California. This gives the students theoretical background for the operational training which follows on prototype power plants located at Idaho Falls, Idaho; West Milton, New York; and Windsor, Connecticut. Up to a point, courses for officers and enlisted men are similar, though the officer's is more advanced—the former are on a graduate level, while the latter are on a college level.

The courses cover the same subject matter in the first four studies —Mathematics, Physics, Heat Transfer, and Fluid Flow and Materials. From this point they diverge. Enlisted students continue with Reactor Principles, Reactor Plant Technology, Radiological Controls, and Operator Specialized Instruction. The officer's course advances to Reactor Plant Engineering, Electrical Engineering, Chemistry, and Radiological Control.

To support the expanding nuclear shipbuilding program, six hundred to eight hundred enlisted personnel enter training each quarter. Here, they are expected to study, and study, and study. Geniuses are welcomed, but not required. The emphasis is on hard work and sincere motivation. The biggest "bear trap" in nuclear training is mathematics, and most of the self-made "geniuses" find it necessary to spend many hours boning-up on mathematics refresher courses. While a strong back is helpful in the Navy, a grasp of calculus is more important in the nuclear program.

When the students are ready for prototype training, they go to a unit with a reactor similar to the type used in the ship for which they are destined. The land-based prototypes at Idaho Falls include those for the *Nautilus* and *Enterprise*. At West Milton are prototypes for the *Triton* and *Bainbridge,* and at Windsor for the submarine *Tullibee*. Some of the qualified reactor operators will go to surface ships, some to submarines, and a few are assigned as instructors.

Included in the crew of a Polaris submarine are thirty-four men directly involved with the Polaris missile system, and an equal number are assigned to operate the nuclear reactor power plant. About one-third work in general service billets having no duties directly connected with the nuclear power plant or the weapon system, such as sonarmen, radiomen, yeomen, storekeepers, cooks, and stewards. Almost all enlisted men are high school graduates, and average twenty-four years of age. They are not only skilled in their trade, but specially trained for duties in a Polaris submarine.

The twelve officers on board include the skipper, executive officer, navigator, engineer officer with three assistants, a weapons system officer and his assistant, communications officer, supply officer, and the ship's doctor. The officers on board must also have special training for FBM submarine duty. Even the ship's doctor is not spared a special course of instruction. For two months he learns about the submarine's reactor and missiles, and spends four more months studying specialized courses in Submarine Medicine, and Nuclear Medicine, Health and Physics.

Specialized medical training has been taught at the Submarine Base in New London/Groton for many years. The rapidly expanding nuclear submarine program imposed a "population explosion" of new students, along with the need for specialized knowledge on the part of physicians and hospital corpsmen. As a result, the Submarine Medical Center was established there in July, 1964 to coordinate all the medical training and research activities.

The six-month course in submarine medicine includes Nuclear Physics, Mathematics, Atmosphere Control, Radiological Monitoring, Psychiatry, Emergency Dentistry, Diving Physiology, and Industrial Toxicology. The high level of medical training is as important to a successful patrol as the reactor machinery and the missiles.

Pushing forward along many nuclear frontiers, the Navy was quick to foresee the need for training medical officers in the virgin territory of nuclear medicine. In 1956, a six-month course in Radioisotope Techniques and Nuclear Medicine was originated at the National Naval Medical Center (NNMC) at Bethesda, Maryland. However, before a course could be initiated, a substantial fund of knowledge was required in this new art. As knowledge and training techniques improved, changes were made in frequency, duration, and curriculum.

Originated for physicians of the U. S. armed forces and other government agencies, the students later included civilian physicians, and those from allied armed forces. Of the 208 graduates through 1964, about three-fourths were radiology physicians, and the others were dentists, nurses, and physicians from numerous foreign countries. From this fountainhead of nuclear medical knowledge, the graduates fanned out around the world, sharing their experience and teaching others.

The medical officers' curriculum at NNMC, in Radioisotope Techniques and Nuclear Medicine, is divided into four basic parts: Radiation Physics, Mathematics, Statistics, and Clinical Laboratory Procedures. In addition to a solid foundation of theory, practical applications are taught, such as "Tumor Localization Using Radioisotopes," "Bone Marrow Transplant," and "Clinical Applications of Organ Photoscanning." A number of the graduates have distinguished themselves in their field, and lecturers are chosen among the country's leading authorities.

The Radioisotope Technician's Course at NNMC extends over a six-month period of concentrated training, including theory and practice. The course consists of Radiation Physics, the inescapable Mathematics, Statistics, Radiation Safety, Chemistry, Chemistry Laboratory Procedures, seventeen phases of Radiation Physics Laboratory, Medical Aspects of NBC Warfare Defense, Clinical Physiology and Procedures in fourteen phases, and Clinical Laboratory Procedures. After concentrated study such as that, one might expect one month of bed rest and recuperation. However, no coddling of the students can be expected from a schedule which allows a mid-day break of one hour for study and lunch, in that order.

The impact of nuclear training has swept through the Navy from

[70]

coast to coast, from seaman to chief petty officer, and from midship-man at the Naval Academy in Annapolis to seasoned officers of the fleet at the Postgraduate School in Monterey, California. Courses range from fundamental studies in nuclear physics and mathematics, to nuclear engineering and nuclear weapons systems.

The Atlantic and Pacific Fleets have established Nuclear Weapons Training Centers—one at Norfolk, and the other at San Diego. These schools supply technically qualified officers and men to handle nuclear weapons, including assembly, testing, storing, monitoring and maintenance. Individual and team training in nuclear weapons handling procedures is taught, and officers are instructed in the employment and operational planning of nuclear weapons.

Both of these training centers are enclosed within a highly secure area because of the classified nature of their subject matter. Specific information concerning nuclear weapons is taught only to those with a high security clearance and a "need to know." The continuous guard around the Nuclear Weapons Training Center at the U.S. Naval Air Station in Coronado, across the bay from San Diego, is augmented by a watch dog named "Lady." It is fortunate that Lady is not relied upon by herself to guard the secrets within the building. Although she has no use for women, whether spies or not, she is a friendly mascot to all men regardless of their security clearance. Lady is out to prove that a dog *is* man's best friend!

Civil Engineer officer's courses are given in Nuclear Defense Construction Engineering and Radiation Shielding at Port Hueneme, California. Atomic, Biological, and Chemical Defense courses are given for all officers at Philadelphia; Treasure Island, California; and at the Army Chemical School, at Fort McClellan, Alabama. Nuclear Emergency Team Training is provided at Albuquerque, New Mexico. Other schools and training centers associated with nuclear weapons are located at Key West, Florida (undersea weapons); Dam Neck, Virginia (guided missile and Polaris training); Indian Head, Maryland (nuclear weapons disposal training); Mare Island, California (guided missiles); and New London/Groton, Connecticut; and Pearl Harbor, Hawaii (Polaris missile training).

Practically every part of the Navy, through every rating structure and operational force, has been affected by the need for knowledge and know-how in the age of atom fragmentation.

If anyone should doubt the ability of American youth to attain excellent standards in this highly technical and complex field, let him talk to the skipper or exec of a nuclear submarine or surface ship. It has been one of the brightest sidelights of the nuclear era to note that our young men, when motivated by an important job requiring great competence and character, will respond splendidly to excellent leadership.

Perhaps the greatest driving force behind the selection and training of our nuclear Navy men is Admiral Rickover, in his capacity as manager of the Naval Reactors Division of the Atomic Energy Commission, and as Assistant Chief of the Bureau of Ships for Nuclear Propulsion. His dynamic leadership in maintaining high standards throughout the expanding nuclear power program has been a herculean effort.

Speaking of Captain Wilkinson, Captain de Poix, Captain Peet, and their combined years of experience in command of our nuclear ships, Admiral Rickover said: "I think the Russians would give a million dollars for them."

Referring to the officers and men in our nuclear power program, Admiral Rickover, in 1959, told a congressional committee: "I am more proud of what these young men have done than I am of what we have done with atomic power. With officers such as these and their highly devoted crews, there is nothing our country cannot do. They are the finest men in the finest military organization in the world.

"When people of their caliber are exposed to the challenge and opportunity of our nuclear power program, the results go beyond all expectations. Not only do we get these outstanding operating crews, but individual officers and sailors go on to do an outstanding job in other parts of the Navy as well.

"For example, about twenty times as many sailors are selected, proportionately, as officer candidates from our nuclear power program than from the entire Navy. One out of every six sailors who has been in the nuclear power program has already been selected for officer programs. Of course, these men represent a loss to the nuclear power program, and an additional training burden to us, but the Navy as a whole benefits immeasurably."

The men who man our nuclear submarines and surface ships have attained a degree of excellence which is unprecedented. Their quality of character and technical competence more than justifies the confidence of the American people in today's men of our nuclear Navy.

SEVEN

Living With the Atom

SWALLOWED BY the steel "whale" which is his home, the submariner is sealed inside an artificial environment, away from his natural surroundings. Of all man's conveyances, the submarine was the first to take him into a medium where, for want of oxygen, he could not long survive. His experiences in exploring the inner space under the sea are the forerunner to living in outer space.

Life in a submarine involves more than the mere process of living in a home. When a nuclear reactor is enclosed inside the pressure hull with 100 to 140 men, the atmosphere must be free of radio-activity, air-conditioned, and purified from hundreds of organic contaminents. Frying bacon, making coffee, washing clothes, and smoking cigars all affect the atmosphere, not to mention machinery lubricants and heat-generating instrument panels. All must be counteracted or neutralized.

In a surface ship the problem is solved by vents circulating fresh air through all compartments. At sea, the simple process of opening a port whisks plenty of bracing salt air into the ship, particularly in office spaces where everything typed in triplicate takes off like a flock of pigeons! The brisk sea breezes also build heavy seas, making the going rough for surface ships as they pitch and roll.

The submariner is spared all the hazards arising from the snappy salt air in exchange for a few hundred problems of atmosphere control peculiar to submersibles. Of course, these problems existed long before the era of nuclear submarines. The first submarines submerged for short periods, and surfaced whenever the red-eyed crew was only partially asphyxiated. In the later diesel-electric submarines, the trick involved providing an acceptable atmosphere for twelve to sixteen hours, or one day at the most.

The nuclear submarine created a need for our scientists, particularly chemists, to create healthful atmospheric conditions for our submariners. Until then, the nuclear submarine could not be completely free of the surface. Three basic considerations in submarine habitability are atmosphere control, radiation safety, and psychological factors. A tremendous effort was required to enable men to live successfully while submerged for weeks or months on end.

The age-old problem of submerging, which affected everyone from Alexander the Great in his diving bell, to Simon Lake and John Holland in their early submarines, was the accumulation of carbon dioxide along with the loss of oxygen. The first diesel-electric submarines could not remain underwater long enough to require renewing the oxygen supply. However, they carried a few cylinders of compressed oxygen, and a carbon dioxide absorbent.

The big problem of atmosphere control when using storage batteries is the build-up of hydrogen—with the ensuing fire hazard. This was solved initially by developing hydrogen detectors. If the concentration of hydrogen approached a dangerous level, a burner could be turned on to burn off the excess. This was an interim measure similar to finding a leaking water pipe and solving the problem by swabbing the deck. "Fixing the leak" was a longer term project; it was solved by producing improved electric batteries which did not emit excessive hydrogen into the air.

The limited endurance of batteries in diesel-electric submarines was supplemented by the snorkel. When raised above the surface, it could be used to blow fresh air throughout a submarine without surfacing, or recharge batteries by drawing in air for the engines.

For many years, the chemists at the Naval Research Laboratory worked on atmosphere control. The end of the 1920s produced soda lime as the carbon dioxide absorbent. In the 1930s, the more effective lithium hydroxide became standard. Chlorate candles were the next improvement. The sodium chlorate decomposes and produces heat. The device looks like a burning candle, and in the process gives off oxygen. These chlorate candles are well adapted for submarine use, since they can be stowed compactly and used with safety. For diesel-electric submarines, atmosphere control had been essentially solved.

The nuclear submarine suddenly imposed a completely new magnitude to the sealed-space habitability problem. Tremendous progress was made with the advent of the *Nautilus, Seawolf,* and *Skate* from 1956 to 1958. Since then, even more advances have reduced air contaminants to one-fifth of what they were.

When *Nautilus'* keel was laid such necessities as continuous oxygen generators and air monitoring and purification equipment were not perfected. Chemico-medical experience factors were nonexistent for conditions prevailing in a submarine where all functions of living and working continue for weeks at a time. Steps taken to solve the atmosphere control problem have been: identifying the chemical materials present; determining the quantity of concentration; comparing the toxicity with the levels present within the submarine; locating the origin of the chemical properties; and devising a means of controlling the concentrations of harmful materials.

While the crew watches a movie in the evening, the smoke from cigarettes, cigars and pipes curls up and blends into a general thick blue haze. The daily concentration of air contamination from tobacco tars and nicotine varies with the routine of activity. In the early mornings, when most of the crew has been sleeping for hours, the concentration is very low. Greater activity about the decks is reflected in the increase of tobacco smoke during afternoons and evenings.

From air samples taken during a nuclear submarine cruise, about 75 per cent of the particulate matter from aerosol samples came from smoking. Although this increases the air purification problem, submariners are allowed the same unlimited smoking as surface ships.

Life on a prolonged cruise below the ocean swells imposes enough restrictions without placing a ban on smoking. Thanks to the continued efforts of the scientists at NRL, submariners can enjoy a cigarette when so many of life's other diversions are denied them.

One of the problems which had the chemists stumped for a while was the source of certain organic compounds found in the submarine atmosphere. Some of the contaminants isolated and analyzed were mineral spirits traced to the copious coatings of oil-based paints covering submarine interiors. Although they were eye-appealing, they were found to have sufficient toxicity to warrant elimination. A water-thinned paint developed at NRL is now commercially available, and submariners can apply new coats of paint to the bulkheads and passageways without introducing the offending mineral spirits. The chemists' war on air contamination from mineral spirits extended to eliminating them for cleaning purposes, and increasing the capacity of carbon beds in the main ventilating system.

Nuclear submarines now have an integrated system for atmosphere control. It is monitored by an atmosphere analyzer which samples the air at several points within a submarine. The air treatment cycle includes the electrostatic precipitator, a catalytic combustion process which oxidizes most organic materials to carbon dioxide and water; a particulate filter to remove dust and other undesirable particles from the air; cooling coils to facilitate absorption of impurities in the carbon bed and extract excess water; activated carbon; carbon dioxide remover, known as the CO_2 scrubber; and the replenishment of oxygen by the O_2 generator.

ESP is usually associated with extrasensory perception. In a submarine it stands for the electrostatic precipitator, an electrically operated filtration device effective in removing aerosol contaminants from the air. Aerosols include many kinds of substances sprayed or vaporized into the atmosphere.

An ESP unit initially was installed in the galley exhaust system of nuclear submarines. The purpose was to remove greasy, oily aerosols

[77]

copiously produced in the galley from cooking around the clock to feed the "hungry hundred." It also eliminated a potential fire hazard. ESP units are now effective in removing aerosol particles from a great variety of locations throughout the submarine.

Air-conditioning is of great importance aboard a submarine. Because of the tremendous heat produced by the nuclear reactor and given off by the associated steam plant, the interior atmosphere must be cooled constantly, and excess moisture removed. Air-conditioning plants installed in the nuclear attack submarines have a capacity for cooling equal to the melting of over two hundred tons of ice per day! Our scientists have strived to provide "fresh country air" from a submarine atmosphere which might otherwise resemble that of the traditional corner pool room.

Living in a submarine poses other problems for the crew. The psychological aspects of prolonged submergence are directly related to their health, comfort, and efficiency, particularly on prolonged cruises. Everything possible is being done to help the submariner extend the time of his submergence to match that of his submarine.

Every crewman likes to have some place to call his own—his bunk and his locker. He sleeps on a foam rubber mattress. He has a fluorescent reading lamp at his bunk. His personal locker is nearby, instead of the old duffle bag which was inadequate, inconvenient, and usually in the way.

Adequate laundry, washroom, and head facilities help remove much of the inconvenience, and eliminate the annoyance of over-crowding and queuing. Plenty of showers and outlets for electric shavers are available. Sufficient water, good lighting, and ventilation also represent some of the simple conveniences of living which make a major difference in habitability. The composite of all these details has a direct bearing on the submariner's limit of endurance. All living accommodations are modern, convenient, and designed to help him tolerate, if not look forward to, long cruises away from home.

The handy little device in the head, known as the toilet, is a fascinating application of the world's composite knowledge of plumbing, physics, hydrodynamics and pressures. In the older submarines, those uninitiated in the mysteries of the salt water flushing system had the educational benefit of a set of instructions posted on the bulkhead. Failure to follow the instructions closely, or a poor sense of timing with the pressures in the flushing process, could produce a surprising sight of man coming out a poor second in his grapple with the machine age.

In the "good old days" of the R and O Class submarines in the 1920s, the inconvenience of using the head was such that the clarion call of nature was often postponed when running submerged. Toilet facilities were frequently rigged topsides where many an *al fresco* balancing contest was lost to Poseidon, god of the rolling sea. Fortunately, the era of the nuclear submarine includes a surprise-free flushing system!

New fixtures and materials have brightened submarine interiors. Extensive use is made of Formica and stainless steel, which are easy to maintain. Pictures that hang on the bulkheads are important, as are the choice of colors and where they are used. In the battle control areas of a submarine, the colors are sharp, contrasting, and well-defined. The lights are brighter, and the texture of control knobs and dials are rough to the touch. A business-like environment is designed to help the operators and watch standers stay alert.

The crew's mess might have yellow bulkheads and green seat covers in contrast to color schemes in other compartments of the submarine. It can be converted from a dining area and rigged for movies, church services, or a general assembly area.

In living spaces, however, reverse psychology is used. Soft, subdued colors are conducive to relaxation. Plaid patterns or other complicated geometrical designs are avoided as overly busy patterns are hard to live with on long cruises and tend to increase sea-sickness.

The latter malady, incidentally, has not been a big problem for nuclear submarines, since they spend much of the time below the rough surface.

All nuclear submarines are capable of remaining below the surface for long periods. The Polaris submarines, in particular, must be geared to long submergence because their constant vigil under the sea demands sixty days or more without surfacing. For this reason, the life of the Polarismen is of particular interest.

The captain of the Gold crew in USS *Thomas A. Edison* (SSBN-610), Comdr. C. D. Grojean, has become accustomed to missing summers and winters in Groton with his family, and never being at home when his children are out of school.

"Getting families mentally adjusted to the periods of prolonged absence is very important," said Commander Grojean, "and makes it easier on the submariner and his family. It is some help to know that plans can be made for months ahead because your schedule is known for a year or more. Besides," he added brightly, "what other career offers a honeymoon every six months?"

Most of the men in Polaris submarines are family men, mature, stable, and highly motivated professional technicians. The sacrifice made by them in terms of family separation is shared by their wives and children. One of the great morale factors in the life of a submariner is the mutual help, understanding, and cooperation between families. This was evident by the personal and financial help given the families following the *Thresher* disaster.

Before leaving on patrol, the head of the household might retile the bathroom, fix the faucets, and put his house in order. Upon returning, he can expect his wife to have another "list of things to be done."

Leaving their families behind and heading out for a patrol area, the crew does not know where they are going; only the skipper knows. They do know that it will be over sixty days before they will again see green grass or blue sky. When the submarine reaches deep water, she disappears from the world we know, and the crew begins the routine of living and working in their artificial microcosm.

In the darkness below, the difference between day and night is determined by the lights on board. White lights are turned on in the daytime, and the ship is "rigged for red" at night. The sun rises and sets in a Polaris submarine with the aid of light switches, usually at sunrise and sunset.

Contact with the outside world is not lost; the vital mission of the Polaris submarine depends on receiving orders to launch missiles if it should ever become necessary. Messages are not sent from the FBM submarines on patrol. Their mission calls for secrecy of position. To keep abreast of world news, radiomen guard the circuits and receive the daily Armed Forces Radio broadcasts, and "familygrams." A "babygram" may announce a new arrival. Dad can pass out a box of cigars to celebrate, but he will have to wait until after the patrol to see the new eight-pound heir and future submariner.

Comdr. Walt Dedrick, former commanding officer of the *Thomas A. Edison* pointed out that "the three 15-word "familygrams" allowed for each man during a patrol are important to the crew's morale. Another big help during family separations is the Personnel Assistance Center, operated by the Chaplain at the submarine base, who looks after the families of Polarismen when they are away from home.

There are no brigs in Polaris submarines, and no discipline problems. The men are selected volunteers, and are well trained and skilled in their specialties. Each Polaris crewman is well aware of the great importance of the job he is doing on patrol—assuring the security of our country.

At sea, watches commence and all hands settle into the daily routine. Missile technicians, sonarmen, nuclear power technicians, and radiomen work in six-hour shifts to provide greater continuity.

[81]

Other ratings such as yeomen, storekeepers, and cooks, are assigned watches to best perform their duties. The crew sheds their regular Navy uniforms in favor of the "jump suit" (blue dacron coveralls). They are comfortable, have no hooks or zippers, and are easy to wash. They are also lint-free, a desirable feature in the highly controlled atmosphere.

One of the most welcome events of the daily routine is "chow down." On board are four cooks, one of whom is the baker. Before they are assigned to a Polaris submarine, they are qualified Navy cooks and are given special training by chefs in the best restaurants and hotels. As a result, they are able to prepare gourmet dishes—shrimp Newburgh, chicken cacciatori, and baked Alaska. Of course, steak, roast beef, and chops are always welcome items on the menu. Instead of the usual "three squares" a day, a fourth meal, "soupdown," is served in mid-afternoon. The ice-cream, popcorn, and coffee makers help ward off hunger pangs in between the four regular meals.

When a Polaris submarine goes down on patrol, it normally takes with it 4,000 pounds of beef, 1,000 pounds of ham, 960 dozen eggs, 3,000 pounds of sugar, 1,200 pounds of coffee, and 120 pounds of tea. The supply officers of Polaris submarines are allowed much freedom in purchasing groceries for the under-way menu. If frozen lobster tails are not included in the approved list, they may nevertheless appear on the table. Since Navy Regulations do not permit spirits on board, however, the submariners cannot wash it down with a vintage Chablis. The serious nature of their mission imposes definite limits to the gustatory pleasures.

The absence of recreational facilities such as baseball diamonds, golf courses, and tennis courts on board submarines suggests a problem in view of the excellent and generous menu. Even when served at sea, excellent food has an insidious way of making clothing shrink, particularly around the waistline. To keep all those calories from getting the upper hand, the *Ethan Allen* has a bicycle and a rowing machine. The former is particularly good for leg muscles, while the latter keeps the waistline trim.

The most prevalent "exercise equipment" is any firm deck where push-ups and sit-ups can be performed. In addition to the "free" athletic equipment, there are barbells, stretch devices, and exercise bicycles, with the added advantage of having no scorekeeper or losers.

By walking around USS *Tecumseh* from stem to stern, it was found that negotiating the vertical ladders and hurdling the high hatch combings left little to be desired exercise-wise. The expenditure of calories was calculated to total a complete chicken dinner topped off with a generous portion of chocolate cake. If the wives back home are not too enthusiastic about the culinary competition from the ship's cooks, it is understandable.

Making use of one's spare time is a great challenge for individual ingenuity. Nevertheless, there is plenty of help in providing opportunities for self-improvement and entertainment during a Polaris patrol. A schedule of activities is made up for each day at sea before an FBM submarine departs her home port.

The scheduled movies are different for every day at sea. They are not all top-notch productions—Hollywood simply does not produce that many A-1 Oscar winners. Whatever the quality, the crew would not want to miss their nightly cinema. Two showings daily (when possible) takes care of the night and day watch-standers. The movie screen provides a brief interlude when the men can join the rest of the world on location in Europe, America or Africa with Cary Grant, Sophia Loren or Doris Day.

Good recreational facilities are part of the armament in the battle against monotony. Chess, acey-deucey, pinochle, bridge, or dozens of other games are played to fill in off-duty moments. Tournaments are often held, and by the end of a patrol a Polaris submarine has a number of "grand champions."

To provide music under the sea, some of the nuclear submarines boast a Hammond organ—not unlike Captain Nemo's mythical *Nautilus*. A record player or tape recorder spins the latest hits, folk songs, or classical music. Usually two or three instrumentalists can be found among the crew who are coaxed to drag a guitar, accordian or trumpet from behind the piping, and cut loose with a few bars of home-made music. Barbershop quartets, sing-along groups, and an occasional brave soloist may produce a talent show to brighten a few hours.

When men are in the mood for reading, they can select books from the ship's library. A variety of titles includes westerns, whodunits, educational reading, or course books for advancement in rating. Polarismen are offered a number of courses for college credit at Harvard University. Textbooks are provided for study, and lectures are on film. Tests, laboratory work, or any part of a course impossible to complete on patrol are finished after the men return to their home port.

Most of the officers and crew accomplish something toward self-improvement during the cruise. One skipper of a Polaris submarine, in addition to keeping up with the latest on nuclear physics, planned to learn to play the guitar on his next patrol.

While excellent cuisine and recreation are fine for morale, spiritual and medical needs are also important. The only semblance of a sick bay on board is an efficiently arranged, closet-sized doctor's office, and the officer's wardroom can be rigged for an emergency operating room. Pre-sailing physical examinations assure the doctor of a one hundred percent hail-and-hearty crew before the submarine is swallowed by the ocean.

Two hospital corpsmen assist the doctor in keeping the men healthy, and in the continuous chores of air and radiation monitoring. Before the start of a patrol, they check to be sure the men do not bring certain kinds of shoe polish, deck wax, or typewriter cleaner on board to foul up the atmosphere with taboo chemical ingredients. The crewmen are well checked out and know better than to wear a wristwatch with a radium dial; it would over-excite the sensitive radiation monitoring instruments.

Polarismen are so self-sufficient during a patrol that they provide their own "clergy" to conduct Sunday church services. Two volunteer lay leaders from the ship's company, usually officers or senior petty officers, are given prior instruction by a Navy chaplain. FBM submarines are equipped with portable organs, altars, and hymnals before going to sea.

When a Polaris submarine surfaces at the end of its strategic watch below, the men make ready for the changeover between the Blue and Gold crews. The first breath of fresh air is not too exhilarating after the controlled air they have been breathing. For months they have been living in a dust-free, hayfeverless atmosphere. When exposed again to the worldwide mixtures of viruses, microbes and allergenic ingredients in the air, the crew usually responds with a profusion of colds and assorted sniffles. These soon pass however, as the crew again gets accustomed to the normal world of men and microbes.

Returning from patrol, the Blue and Gold crews work together during a short turnover period. This is normally accomplished alongside a Polaris submarine tender at an advanced location such as Holy Loch, Scotland. The crews travel to and from their home port by bus and jet planes, giving them almost three months out of six at home.

The new crew takes over and disappears for another watch under the sea. Whether they are Polarismen or serving in an attack submarine, crews can now match the endurance of the nuclear reactor, and live with the atom for as long as their mission requires.

EIGHT

Hunting and Hiding Below— Antisubmarine Warfare

THE BIGGEST cat and mouse game in the world is the hunt for submarines concealed in the greatest hiding place on earth—the depths of the sea. Dark and deep, the oceans challenge both the hunter and the hunted.

Before the advent of the nuclear-powered submarine, surface ships had a great advantage over submarines. Once detected, it was a matter of depth charging until the submarine was either destroyed or until the contact was lost. If contact could be maintained over a sufficient period of time, the submarine would be forced to surface. Out-gunned and unable to out-maneuver a destroyer-type adversary, the surfaced submarine was in a perilous position.

Nuclear-powered submarines can speed away quickly and remain submerged indefinitely. In fact, the speed of a submerged nuclear submarine may be greater than the surface ship pursuing it, particularly in heavy seas when the going is slow and there are poor sonar conditions. Since noise often accompanies speed, the faster a submarine goes the louder her signals are, telegraphing her position. This is also true of surface antisubmarine warfare (ASW) ships. New techniques have therefore been imposed to detect and track high-speed, long-range nuclear submarines.

Paradoxically, the nuclear submarine itself has become one of the best ASW ships. With speed, range, and improved detection equipment, she can employ her sensory devices deep down in the same ele-

[86]

ment as her adversary, without intervening thermal layers of water to distort sonar signals.

Although considered to be running blind when submerged, submarines actually enjoy the same opacity of deep water as a means of running unseen by an enemy. Blindness in the depths goes two ways, for submarine and antisubmarine—with one exception. When a skipper chooses, he can up-periscope briefly to add vision to his other sensory means. The laws of physics are definitely on the side of the submarine when shielded by the sea.

To eliminate the sounds generated by movement, a submarine can rest quietly and indefinitely on the bottom, if it does not exceed its test depth. Or it can hover with neutral buoyancy at a relatively safe depth where detection is extremely difficult. Noise also radiates through the water from surface ships and the sonars of submarines are able to detect them from a considerable distance.

If the submarine is a nuclear one, it is free to outrun conventionally powered ASW surface forces. Distance and thermal layers of water tend to complicate sonar evaluation, and thus search sonars are not very effective at high speeds. By their very existence, nuclear submarines have created a much greater ASW problem.

The limitations inherent in ASW surface forces operating alone gave birth to the hunter-killer team. Since almost everything in the Navy acquires an acronymic name, the hunter-killer group is known as a "HUK" group. It is composed of an aircraft carrier (CVS) as the flagship, destroyers, submarines, helicopters, and carrier- and land-based aircraft. On an ASW mission, HUK groups employ DASH, MAD, VDS, SUBROC, ASROC, ASTOR, plus other combinations of the alphabet. When used collectively, this "word game" spells improved submarine hunting.

In order to increase the detection range of a HUK group, aircraft are equipped with Magnetic Anomaly Detection (MAD) gear. When flying area patterns, aircraft so equipped can cover many square miles in ASW surveillance missions. Rather than fight the laws of physics in solving underwater sound problems, MAD gear is a method of detection by which interruptions in the magnetic lines of force, by some big metal object like a submarine, signal an alert for closer investigation.

One means of investigation is by VDS (Variable Depth Sonar). By lowering a sound dome into the water below confusing layers of varying water temperatures (thermal layers), the direction, distance, and movement of a submarine can be detected. A VDS device can be lowered from a destroyer-type ship, and dunking sonar can be rigged from a helicopter. Nuclear-attack submarines with a prime mission of ASW have built-in VDS, because a submersible can seek whatever depth is required to hunt another submarine.

DASH is a new type of stand-off weapon from a small helicopter landing deck on an ASW destroyer. Its expanded name means Drone Anti-Submarine Helicopter. This small, unmanned helicopter takes off from the landing platform carrying a homing torpedo. Controlled from the destroyer, it reaches far out across the water over a submarine contact, releases its torpedo, and drops it into the water at the right attitude (nose first) with the aid of a small parachute.

The drone helicopter, having delivered its lethal load, is then radio-guided back to its destroyer landing platform—like a homing pigeon coming back to roost. This permits the destroyer to deliver a potent weapon from a distance. Approaching to a closer range, the destroyer might herself become a prize target. DASH also has the advantage of dropping the weapon at a distant point quicker than the destroyer could deliver depth charges, hedge hogs, or other short-range ASW weapons. When opposed by a nuclear submarine, the ability to project explosives quickly is a decided advantage.

As the number of nuclear submarines increases, the need for improved detection and stand-off destruction of submarines must also increase. New, lightweight, acoustic-homing torpedoes, and weapon Able are other distant submarine killers used in the fleet. The latter is a long-range antisubmarine rocket that is fired from a launcher, much as a shell is fired from a gun. These weapons are designed for conventional warheads.

A target worthy of a nuclear explosion must have great intrinsic value, or pose a threat serious enough to warrant the expenditure of a nuclear warhead. A nuclear submarine qualifies as a worthy target for a nuclear weapon on both counts. In any nation's ledger book, it is an expensive and complex weapons platform. Far overriding the value consideration is the great threat which nuclear submarines now pose. The enormous destructive power and long-range of weapons launched from nuclear submarines causes concern which extends to all military and industrial targets. The submarine threat is no longer confined to the seas.

One of our most spectacular ASW weapons is SUBROC—a submarine-launched rocket. Rear Adm. W. T. Hines, former Deputy Chief of the Bureau of Naval Weapons, has stated that, in wartime; "Enemy submarines would be a definite challenge to the free world's use of vital shipping lanes. In addition, with the advent of missile-firing submarines, the protection of our coastal cities becomes a problem of the highest priority. The Navy is meeting this threat with the development of weapons systems such as SUBROC, which promises to be of utmost importance in combating the submarine menace."

SUBROC is a missile launched horizontally underwater through a standard torpedo tube in an attack submarine. At a safe distance from the submarine, the rocket motor ignites and thrusts the missile upward. Once free of the water, the rocket motor separates from the rest of the missile. A guidance system and automatic controls regulate the flight of the nuclear-depth missile. It re-enters the water at supersonic speed, where the nuclear warhead explodes and destroys the nearby enemy submarine.

An underwater-to-underwater missile, SUBROC can be used at long range. A submarine-launched, rocket-propelled, inertially guided, solid-fuel missile, SUBROC weighs approximately four thousand pounds. It is highly accurate and uses a rapid, digitized system of fire control which can also be used on other submarine-launched weapons.

Some of the advantages of this ASW weapon make it particularly adaptable for submarines to handle. SUBROC is carried "dormant" in torpedo tubes for long periods and can be launched with very little preparation on short notice. It has maximum safety features, and requires no special launching tubes and little extra handling equipment.

The high speed of SUBROC is capable of placing it on target before an enemy submarine is able to take evasive action. The system can also detect submarines at great distances and can fire the missiles in rapid order. In addition to reaching targets in normal situations, it is able to attack areas that are inaccessible to ships, such as a well-protected bay area. Indeed, SUBROC is a weapon geared in every way to the realities of modern nuclear undersea warfare.

Those organizations principally involved in developing the SUBROC system were the Navy's Bureau of Weapons, the Naval Ordance Laboratory, Goodyear Aerospace Corporation, and the Naval Ordance Test Station (NOTS) at Pasadena and China Lake, California. The USS *Permit* completed a successful major testing program of SUBROC's capabilities during operations in the Pacific in 1963.

ASROC, a running mate of SUBROC, means Anti-Submarine Rocket. A surface-to-underwater missile, it has many features similar to SUBROC, although it was designed to be launched from surface ships.

ASTOR, a fast, silent-running, electric torpedo, is another weapon with a long reach. The twenty-foot long ASTOR weighs over a ton and can be fired from nuclear and conventionally powered submarines. Its effective range cannot yet be divulged. It is designed to destroy high-speed, deep-running submarines or surface ships at distances beyond the reach of any previously used torpedo in the fleet.

In World War II, submarines were occasionally used to knock out enemy submarines. However, the "kills" were conducted in much the same way as a submarine attack on surface ships. In every case the target submarines were operating on the surface when attacked, probably in the process of recharging their batteries. At that time submarines were not equipped to fight each other in the submerged battle condition for which they were designed.

After World War II, the conventionally powered submarines already in existence were modernized with snorkeling equipment and streamlined. The USS *Albacore* was the first submarine built with the new whale-shaped hull, and hydronamic qualities, giving her a spectacular increase in speed and maneuverability. The *Albacore* shape was first joined with nuclear power in USS *Skipjack*. The aquabatics of the new submarines ushered in a new phase to submarining—"Fasten your seatbelts."

The 1950's brought a redirection of effort in submarine warfare aimed specifically toward ASW. The emergence of the nuclear-powered submarine signaled the greatest step forward. In January, 1955, when *Nautilus* became the first to submerge on nuclear power, it was a great triumph from the standpoint of capabilities and opportunities. However, it also posed a great new problem for antisubmarine forces whose task was already a rather "sticky wicket."

Nuclear-attack submarines assumed new missions, including the primary task of ASW. Nuclear power was not alone responsible for this new mission. Improved sonars, weapons, and techniques kept pace until the modern *Thresher*-class submarines evolved as a most formidable ASW weapon system. The system includes hunting, detecting, localizing, classifying, and destroying enemy submarines. This requires not a mere weapon, but a fully integrated weapons system coordinated by a team of highly skilled officers and men.

A successful submarine operation includes the combination of secrecy, silence, surprise, sustained speed, staying ability, striking power and deep submergence. Our nuclear submarines are strong in all of these essential qualities, and sustained speed underwater is certainly one of their strongest features. Silence is difficult to attain under the sea where silence is golden. However, new methods of noise reduction have been developed. Deeper submergence increases the operating area throughout the vast ocean, and makes detection more difficult. Staying ability allows a submarine to remain submerged as long as required, and an ASW force would not be able to flush the submarine to the surface.

Striking power has increased many times over World War II weapons. Polaris, Regulus, SUBROC, and improved torpedoes and mines present a new magnitude of offensive strength, particularly when coupled with the capabilities of our nuclear submarines.

Teamwork is a necessity, not only between all elements of our HUK groups, but also between our naval forces and those of our allied navies. The greater challenge of our nuclear age has placed an even greater reliance on team effort.

In the ASW struggle, the attack submarine is not alone. An ASW aircraft carrier (CVS) is the key ship in a HUK group. Unfortunately, we do not have an all-nuclear surface force to keep pace with our nuclear attack submarines. Since many of the submarines to be hunted may be nuclear-powered, it would be desirable to have nuclear-powered ASW ships.

Capt. Vincent Paul de Poix, who first commanded the nuclear attack carrier *Enterprise* (CVAN-65), stated before the Joint Committee on Atomic Energy: "One of the very best submarine tactics a surface skipper can use is continuous high speed—a most effective maneuver. A nuclear carrier can do this with comparative impunity. A conventional carrier cannot, without reducing the period between refuelings.

"In addition to this there are other tactics which we have developed and which we have added to our ability to evade subs. One was in operating down off Cuba. We knew there were subs in the area. We knew it was to our distinct advantage to move around as fast as we could and to change the scene of our operations between day or night operation. So, at every opportunity we would steam at high speed to change our position to another area. The conventional carrier could do the same thing but not without additionally depleting her black oil."

Destroyers, too, are a most important part of the HUK team. Because the destroyer types are multipurpose ships, they must carry weapons to counter air and surface attack as well as knocking out submerged targets. They now have oil-burning steam plants, and are dependent on a carrier for frequent topping off of their oil bunkers. Until nuclear-powered destroyers are designed and built, the full advantage of a nuclear ASW carrier cannot be realized.

The USS *Bainbridge* followed by the USS *Truxton* will be the first two frigates able to track an enemy nuclear submarine and stay with it day after day, and week after week. More nuclear destroyer leaders are needed to match nuclear submarines in endurance and sustained speed. Conceding the advantages of nuclear power to enemy submarines by employing only conventionally powered surface ships to oppose them, is a concession no major power can afford. Building a large number of nuclear ships like the *Bainbridge* and *Truxton* may be expensive, but the cost of not having them is prohibitive.

Capt. Raymond E. Peet, who commanded the *Bainbridge,* said in a congressional hearing: "We haven't really begun to develop the possibilities of *Bainbridge.* We have developed a little in the ASW business which I think has a tremendous future for nuclear-powered ships. In an amphibious exercise, we were located 300 to 400 miles to the north. We were not to be part of this exercise, but when they needed additional ASW support we were sent. We could transit at high speeds. We got there about twelve hours ahead of anybody else.

[93]

"Within six hours after we got there, we picked up a sub that was in the attacking force and were able to put him out of action. This was a case where possibly the mission would have failed if we had not had a ship to get there and do the job. If I am going to operate with nuclear submarines, I would like to be able to stay with them."

Vice Adm. John S. Thach, one of the Navy's top authorities on ASW, is also one of its most eloquent spokesmen. He summed up the submarine threat with the following:

"Today, the Soviet Navy's construction program is firmly focused on nuclear power and rockets. They have a growing number of nuclear-powered submarines in operation, both in the Pacific and in the Atlantic. They have ballistic missiles on a number of conventionally powered boats. The number is growing. They assert that they have fired ballistic missiles from submerged submarines. I know of no reason to doubt them.

"Missile-firing submarines are not our only concern. The capability of the Russian's long-range, fast-attack submarine to conduct offensive actions in the Atlantic, Pacific, Indian and Arctic oceans poses a serious menace to free world commerce and naval operations. The threat inherent in about four hundred Communist conventional submarines is, in itself, formidable.

"The true nuclear submersible which no longer needs to expose herself on the surface of the seas, represents a much tougher problem. Her ability to dive to unprecedented depths, coupled with fantastic improvements in maneuverability and speed, have compounded the difficulties of detection and tracking. Her nearly unlimited endurance has expanded the area of offensive to the seventy percent of the earth's surface that is water. Soviet submarines now can remain in patrol stations off both our coasts indefinitely. They can also conduct operations in the Arctic. The difficulties of carrying out ASW among the ice packs needs no elaboration.

"It is to this threat that our ASW effort must be directed if we are to remain able to project and exploit our naval power."

[94]

Nuclear power has given submarines a great advantage over antisubmarine forces. The hunting is harder and the hiding is better. It will take continued, concerted, and concentrated effort for years before ASW concepts fully close the gap. One thing is clear. We cannot rely on World War II methods to combat the ASW problem in the nuclear era. A team effort between the Navy, science, and industry is needed to solve the biggest ASW problem—the nuclear-powered submarine.

NINE

Nuclear Combatants on the Sea

On December 2, 1957, the keel was laid for a prototype nuclear cruiser. She was destined to become USS *Long Beach,* the world's first nuclear-powered surface combatant ship. She was also the first of three nuclear-propelled surface ships, including the attack aircraft carrier USS *Enterprise,* and the guided-missile destroyer leader USS *Bainbridge.*

These ships, of three different types, were placed in commission within a year's time. By building three different prototypes, the Navy was able to gain the maximum amount of information and operational experience. Each ship benefitted in a different way from nuclear power, while all gained the longer endurance of nuclear fuel.

Their characteristics and performance were observed with great interest. Future design and policy hinged on whether these ships "proved out" in actual operations with the fleet. New, spectacular standards of performance were expected and set such as the Navy had never known.

Nuclear power made a spectacular advance in submarining. However, the advantages for surface ships took longer to realize. The need for extended, high-speed steaming is just as important for surface ships as it is for submarines. Greater average operational speeds required of our surface ships necessitates more frequent refueling. Nuclear power offers the only hope of eliminating these persistent interruptions of operations, and the logistical problems that go with them.

Experience has confirmed that the ocean is ideally suited for nuclear-powered surface ships as well as for submarines. Long stretches of open water from port to port and continent to continent are perfectly scaled for the use of long-range, sustained nuclear power. The size of ships in mass and weight provides a worthy vehicle for nuclear energy, whether a voyage is from New York to Naples, or San Francisco to Hong Kong. The oceans provide safety by their remoteness from populated areas. Furthermore, what better coolant medium does the world have to offer than the vast reaches of sea water—three hundred and forty million cubic miles of it, give or take a few million.

Traditionally, cruisers have always been required to roam over large areas, and must be able to go beyond the vicinity of a task force. Nuclear power extends their cruising range far beyond that attainable by oil-burning cruisers. The characteristic of this type of ship, as its name implies, is the ability to cruise at long range. Certainly no ship ever lived up to her name with greater emphasis than USS *Long Beach*. Her unprecedented cruising range is measured in terms of months rather than miles, and freedom from the end of the oil hose makes her capable of independent global operations.

The *Long Beach* has chalked up a number of interesting "firsts." She was the first cruiser designed and built from the keel up since the end of World War II. Every other cruiser in the Navy is a ship of World War II conception and design. Although a number have been converted into missile cruisers with modernized electronic systems associated with their weapons, *Long Beach* was the first to be designed for, and armed with, guided missiles as her main battery. Her first commanding officer was also the first to command USS *Nautilus*, Capt. Eugene P. Wilkinson.

Our first nuclear-powered surface ship, *Long Beach* (CGN-9) was built at the Fall River Shipyard of the Bethlehem Steel Company at Quincy, Massachusetts. She was commissioned on September 9, 1961. The ship's basic statistics of 16,400 tons displacement, 721 feet in overall length, and a complement of over 1,000 officers and men, are not far different from other cruisers of the fleet. However, her twin nuclear reactors give *Long Beach* a maximum range of 720 nautical miles per day—day after day.

The ship's independence of other naval forces includes her versatile weapons which are capable of destroying targets in the air, on the surface, or under the sea. These include the Terrier and Talos missiles, and the ASROC, in addition to the more conventional five-inch guns and torpedo tubes. This array of far-reaching, powerful missiles and weapons makes the nuclear cruiser a one-ship task force when required, to destroy enemy ships, shore installations, aircraft, or submarines.

The unusual appearance of the *Long Beach* is partly due to her nuclear power plant, and lack of smoke stacks. The absence of the traditional main-battery gun turrets belies the explosive power hidden in the compartments behind her missile launchers. To further disarm the casual viewer, *Long Beach* apparently lacks the radar capability of most combatant ships. This is a false impression. Instead of the familiar radar antennae which seem to crowd every available space on the masts and superstructure of our other ships, *Long Beach* has radars built into the superstructure as an integral part of the ship's design.

The clean lines of the nuclear cruiser are the result of basic ship design catching up with the electronic-nucleonic age, and undoubtedly marks a trend toward cleaner, uncluttered, and streamlined ships of the future. USS *Long Beach* is a brave, bold departure from cruisers of the past, but she is only the beginning of the Navy's new breed of nuclear-powered surface combatants.

The USS *Enterprise* CVA(N)-65 is clear evidence of the preeminence of the United States in developing and using nuclear energy. If any American is concerned about the prestige of the United States in world affairs, it is hoped that he can experience a surge of pride in his country should he be visiting a foreign city when the *Enterprise* steams into port. Although this same pride is inspired by all of our big, grey fighting ships, there is something special about the power and majesty of the *Enterprise*—equal to a twenty-five-story building from keel to mast top!

When the USS *Enterprise* was commissioned on November 25, 1961, the U.S. Navy acquired the world's largest and most spectacular combatant ship. The nuclear-powered attack carrier was placed in commission two-and-a-half months after the commissioning pennant was hoisted in the cruiser *Long Beach*. If any ship of the Navy could be accused of cornering the market on superlatives, it would have to be USS *Enterprise*.

What makes this great ship tick is a story of scientific engineering and industrial achievement. Built at the Newport News Shipbuilding Company in Virginia, *Enterprise* has a displacement of 85,350 tons, spread over her 1,123-foot length. Her 474-million-dollar cost includes eight nuclear reactors, representing the world's largest nuclear power complex. These reactors provide over 200,000 horsepower that spins her four 21-foot-diameter propellers, each weighing 64,500 pounds.

Capt. Vincent Paul de Poix, the first *Enterprise* skipper, expressed great confidence in the ship's reactors: "The conservatism built into the reactors is one feature that gives us additional reliability. These reactors are so well built that we never expect to, and never have, trouble with them, although, of course, we are ready at any time to cope with a problem if it occurs."

The potential electric generating capacity would supply power for a city of over two million people, and is carried through the ship by six hundred and twenty-five miles of electrical cable. The horsepower generated by her fissioning nuclear fuel gives *Enterprise* a speed of over thirty-four knots, and a daily maximum range of over eight hundred and twenty nautical miles. This boils down to one simple characteristic of this nuclear aircraft carrier—unprecedented mobility.

The *Enterprise* is a floating, nuclear-powered city of forty-six hundred officers and men, with the air group aboard. About fourteen thousand meals are prepared each day in the two large crew galleys, five smaller galleys, a bakery, and two butcher shops. Ten to twelve tons of food are consumed daily! Meals are served at sea during nineteen of the twenty-four hours, and there are three "gedunk stands" where the crew can purchase a soda.

Some of the rather unexpected facilities on board include basketball courts, and a TV station which can transmit to other ships in company at sea. Lest the ladies think that they are excluded from the nuclear age, four ladies' powder rooms are located in the ship. In this modern city, the nuclear carrier has shops which ply the ancient trades such as blacksmith, carpenter, and cobbler.

The bluejacket of the "old Navy" who slept in a hammock and stowed his gear in a ditty bag would hardly recognize his seagoing life on board the *Enterprise*. All the berthing compartments and most of the working spaces are air-conditioned. (Portholes are unnecessary. The only three on board are in the captain's cabin, mounted for sentimental reasons. They were salvaged from the famous World War II *Enterprise*.) Each bunk has an outlet adjustable to the individual "climate" desired, a foam rubber mattress, and a reading lamp. The old Navy may have had a few books and dog-eared copies of the *Police Gazette;* on the *Enterprise* there is a selection of seven thousand books in the ship's library. The "old salt" would be even more amazed to hear music piped to all living and messing compartments throughout the ship, and to see the approximately ninety television sets on board.

Religious services are held every Sunday on the hangar deck, or in the ship's Memorial All-Faiths Prayer Chapel. There are many Christian truths which stand firm despite changes brought by nuclear reactors or whatever may next flow out of the scientific ferment of our exciting age. Fantastic as USS *Enterprise* may be, it is certain that only good, dedicated men can make her the great ship she is.

Enterprise is geared to the nuclear era in many ways, including her medical department. A staff of six doctors specialize in Aviation Medicine, Surgery, Radiobiology, and Internal Medicine. They are assisted by forty-eight Hospital Corpsmen who help run the eighty-six-bed sick bay, the modern medical laboratory, and the pharmacy. There are four personnel decontamination stations to care for casualties resulting from atomic, biological, or chemical attack, and a staff of health physics technicians headed by a Radiological Control Officer. Their job is to conduct an active program of monitoring personnel spaces to maintain radiation control.

The non-nuclear phases of medicine must continue as attested by the annual count of "visits" to sick bay, where eight thousand blood tests, ten thousand X rays, and twenty thousand immunizations are given, in addition to daily sick call and hospital admissions. The flight surgeons and Hospital Corpsmen maintain constant watch on the flight deck during air operations to render quick assistance in case of accidents.

One of the hazards of high-performance aircraft is the noise level from the screaming jet aircraft. Although flight deck crewmen who work in proximity to the jets wear ear plugs and "Mickey Mouse"-type ear protectors, repeated tests are made to insure that their auditory acuity has not diminished. A ten-man, sound-proof, simultaneous audiometric screening booth is used to pursue the on-board hearing conservation program.

However noisy, the *Enterprise*'s "main battery" consists of modern high-performance aircraft. These include jet and prop planes, able to deliver a variety of weapons over a wide spectrum of air missions. The supersonic F4B Phantom II, a world's speed record-holder of over sixteen hundred miles per hour, is a two-man, twin-engine interceptor. It can destroy enemy aircraft in all weather conditions with Sparrow III or Sidewinder missiles.

The F8E Crusader, also supersonic, is a single-seat fighter interceptor which fires rockets, cannon, or Sidewinder missiles. The

RF8A version of the Crusader is used for photographic reconnaissance. The third supersonic aircraft in the ship's "arsenal" is the A5A Vigilante, a swept-wing, twin-engine jet, weighing over twenty-two tons, and capable of speeds in excess of Mach two. Carrying a pilot and bombardier-navigator, she can deliver conventional or atomic weapons over a target ahead of the sound of her approach.

A smaller jet attack aircraft, the A4C Skyhawk, is a single-seat plane of subsonic speed with a versatile capability in delivering nuclear or conventional weapons. The specialist in the low-and-slow delivery, so important to limited warfare situations, is the A1H Skyraider. She is a propeller-driven, single-seater, particularly adapted for low-level attack in the two-hundred-mile-per-hour speed range.

The squadron on board providing the long-range surveillance over the "area of operations" flies the EIB Tracer. This all-weather, twin-engine aircraft provides airborne early-warning to fleet or shore complexes. Its eighteen-foot radome (radar dome), mounted above the fuselage, carries part of the far-seeing radar eyes of the fleet.

Approximately one hundred aircraft, operating from *Enterprise*, are assisted in take-off by four steam-driven catapults. They can launch aircraft at the rate of one every fifteen seconds from the four-and-one-half-acre flight deck! Even the big twenty-two-ton Vigilante can be launched from a standing position to one hundred and sixty miles per hour in only two hundred and fifty feet! This quick take-off is carefully controlled so no harmful "G" forces are imparted to the pilot, or damaging stress imposed on the aircraft. A concrete strip one mile long would be required for the same kind of aircraft to make a normal take-off on land. Steam for the four catapults is supplied by heat from the nuclear reactors.

The reactors also supply electrical power for her gigantic electronic requirements, including the energizing of one million tubes, transistors, and diodes. The ship's total electronic equipment is equal to the output of three hundred major radio stations operating simultaneously.

Nuclear Combatants on the Sea

Data processing has gone to sea with a modern, speedy, computer and communications system called the Naval Tactical Data System (NTDS). It was developed to answer the need for processing multiple, high-speed attacks from missiles, aircraft, or other threats. In modern warfare, when speed of thousands of miles per hour must be dealt with, there is little time for deliberations before counterattack.

By doing the thinking ahead of time, and computing it, the NTDS can anticipate simultaneous, high-speed attacks from various directions and altitudes with incredible speed. It gathers uncorrelated information from a number of sources, runs it through data processing "electronic brains," and performs the functions of detection, location, tracking, speed, identity, size, and number of enemy forces. The transistorized computers figure out the correct answers instantaneously, and display them automatically on the scopes installed in the Combat Information Center (CIC). Fleet commanders then are able to comprehend quickly the overall situation and respond with commands to employ the most effective weapons.

The NTDS is interconnected with computer installations on other ships within the task force. In this way the task force commander, as well as his subordinate commanders, are constantly provided with the overall tactical situation the instant it develops.

Before NTDS, the men on watch in CIC were required to plot the entire combat situation with grease pencil markings. In a rapidly changing attack, particularly with more than one raid approaching, the plotting team is constantly kept busy erasing and marking new positions. This situation inspired the remark "How about that—a multimillion dollar electronic system and a million dollar missile, connected by a ten-cent grease pencil?"

NTDS incorporates a display of the situation without the time lag inherent in the plotting system. The Navy can afford the ten-cent grease pencil, but not the delay that goes with it in high-speed modern warfare when supersonic delivery of nuclear weapons is possible.

[103]

A nuclear aircraft carrier has so many advantages that the skippers and flag officers who have worked with *Enterprise* cannot conceal their enthusiasm. However, when a nuclear carrier must rely on conventionally powered escort ships, the advantage is not unlike a mother-in-law escort on a honeymoon. The oil-hose shackles were not fully released from the *Enterprise* until the nuclear destroyer leader USS *Bainbridge* enabled her to run free at a moment's notice, in response to crises anywhere in the world.

For many decades, the all-purpose workhorse of the Navy has been the destroyer. With the commissioning of USS *Bainbridge* DLG(N)-25, on October 6, 1962, the "greyhounds of the fleet" emerged into the nuclear age. The twin nuclear reactors of our first nuclear destroyer leader give her a range of over seven hundred and twenty nautical miles a day, and will permit her years of high-speed steaming without refueling.

It is axiomatic that nuclear-attack carriers, to be fully mobile, should have escort destroyers as tactically free of the fuel problem as they are. The first carrier skipper to enjoy a nuclear escort, Captain de Poix said: "I don't think there is any question about the fact that a nuclear task force is better than a hybrid task force where you have a nuclear carrier and conventional escorts. When we were able to steam, as we did on two or three very interesting occasions, with the *Bainbridge*, it was sheer delight to have an escort with us that was able to steam right with us."

At a cost of one hundred and sixty million dollars, the USS *Bainbridge* was the most expensive destroyer-type we had ever built. She is also the largest, having an overall length of five hundred and sixty-four feet and weighing in at eighty-four hundred tons. A guided missile ship with advanced electronics, she is modern in every way. *Bainbridge* is a multipurpose ship, loaded down with radars, electronic systems, and new weapons to reach farther into the sky and under the water. Her communications equipment would have amazed Marconi.

One of the inevitable results of installing modern and complicated equipment has been an increase in the size of destroyer leaders to about one-third larger than World War II destroyers. They are now in a size category adaptable to nuclear propulsion. This is fortunate because it also produces unlimited auxiliary power for the heavy demands made on electrical and electronic equipment.

In a historical parallel, our Navy's first destroyer was USS *Bainbridge* (DD-1), and our first nuclear-powered destroyer bears the same name. The span of years between the commissioning of the first destroyer in 1902, and the nuclear-powered *Bainbridge*, marks the progress of our destroyer force during the first sixty years of the twentieth century. The old *Bainbridge*, a four-hundred-and-twenty-ton destroyer, was only two hundred and fifty feet from bow to stern. Her ungainly appearance was marked by a low freeboard, with sea water usually boiling over her weather deck, and dominated by four large stacks. Although she was the best of her day, she presents a sharp contrast to the modern *Bainbridge* of our nuclear Navy.

The nuclear *Bainbridge* has a high clipper bow with excellent sea-keeping qualities. She has twin missile launchers fore and aft with associated directors, an ASROC launcher forward of the bridge, and a low superstructure with two radar masts. Her uncluttered deck dips to a lower level at the stern, forming a flight deck area for her helicopters. She is able to steam at twenty knots around the world approximately twenty times without refueling, giving her global mobility and constant readiness.

The ship's first skipper, Capt. Raymond E. Peet, stated it well: "Nuclear power in a destroyer does give you another dimension. We talk of readiness. Our job is to be ready to do whatever we need to do. We know the reactors are ready at a moment's notice. We always have full power on the line. All we have to do is open the throttle and go. You can accelerate in a hurry. You can go from dead stop to full speed and stop again. You can do this as many times as you want to with a nuclear power plant. I don't care whether it is India, South

America, South Africa—anyplace. It is ready to go as fast as it takes me to pull in the lines and get going."

The Navy formed its first all-nuclear task force in the spring of 1964, when *Long Beach* and *Bainbridge* joined the *Enterprise* in the Mediterranean. Operating as part of the Sixth Fleet, these three nuclear ships operated together for the first time on May 13, 1964, to form Task Group 60.1. *Enterprise,* commanded by Capt. Frederick H. Michaelis, was also the flagship of Rear Adm. Bernard M. Strean, the Task Group Commander. Captains Frank H. Price, Jr. and Raymond E. Peet commanded the *Long Beach* and *Bainbridge* respectively.

The *Bainbridge* and *Enterprise* had operated together with the Sixth Fleet during the summer of 1963. However, the nuclear carrier had never "rubbed noses" with the *Long Beach.* The two ships met for the first time while relieving units of the Sixth Fleet in the Mediterranean in August, 1963. To test the comparative maneuvering characteristics of these two big nuclear ships, they conducted competitive exercises which had all the earmarks of a mid-ocean drag race. Asking a sailor from either ship when the other is superior is a good way to set off a non-nuclear explosion!

The Sixth Fleet is a mobile, self-reliant and versatile naval force, able to operate indefinitely at sea without shore bases in the Mediterranean. Task Group 60.1 is perfectly suited for operations with the Sixth Fleet since it requires minimum logistical dependence over long periods. The long-range capabilities of the all-nuclear Task Group 60.1 have dwarfed the length and breadth of the Mediterranean Sea to that of a mere pond. Nuclear-powered ships require a larger geographical stage to demonstrate their mobile possibilities.

It was quite natural that our first three nuclear surface ships should burst out into a larger global orbit. When Admiral Strean welcomed the *Long Beach* and *Bainbridge* to the Mediterranean, he sent a message from the *Enterprise:* "We have looked forward to this moment when we can begin demonstrating the strategic mobility and unlimited endurance of these twentieth century ships." This they set out to do in a most convincing way.

After operations with the Sixth Fleet, the three nuclear ships of Task Group 60.1 passed Gibraltar on July 31, 1964, and headed down the west coast of Africa. Rounding the Cape of Good Hope, they operated together in the Indian Ocean before steaming into Karachi, India. This completed the first leg of Operation Sea Orbit, and set a new world's record for the longest non-stop cruise without refueling for surface ships—more than eleven thousand nautical miles. This record was set inadvertently, and hardly began to demonstrate the full reach of our nuclear ships.

The *Enterprise, Long Beach,* and *Bainbridge* continued on to Australia, making single-ship calls at Freemantle, Melbourne, and Sydney before clearing Cape Horn, and steaming northward along the eastern coast of South America. They encountered two winters and two summers en route, returning to their home ports in autumn, on October 5, 1964. Included in their variety of climate and geography were the monsoon season of the Indian Ocean, the foul weather of forty degrees south latitude called the "roaring forties," and the iceberg armada of the Antarctic. Nevertheless, almost daily air operations were conducted en route.

During the entire cruise, the ships made a speed of more than twenty knots, and were completely independent of any kind of logistic support. The space normally required by black oil was used for aviation fuel, ammunition, food supplies, and spare parts during the 30,500-mile voyage.

Thousands of foreign visitors and dignitaries were welcomed abroad the *Enterprise, Long Beach,* and *Bainbridge* during Operation Sea Orbit. However, the globe-girdling cruise was more than a goodwill tour. It demonstrated the new strategic reinforcement capability of an all-nuclear Task Group in a world beset by widely separated crises. It is a big step forward in the Navy's ability to exert the influence of the United States anywhere in the world, through our nuclear combatants on the sea.

TEN

The Battle Between Atoms and Oil

IT IS DIFFICULT to believe that after the commissioning of the nuclear attack carrier *Enterprise*, the next two attack carriers to be built retrogressed from nuclear power back to oil! During the years from 1958 to 1964, nuclear propulsion had made dramatic improvements unmatched in any other type of power production. The new attack carrier *John F. Kennedy* (CVA-67) could have benefitted from improved nuclear power. The cost of the initial nuclear reactor fuel cores had been cut in half, at the same time doubling their lives. Only four reactors would have been required, instead of the eight installed in the *Enterprise*.

Tremendous progress was made in surface nuclear propulsion plants, in cost and simplification of operation, under the direction of Vice Admiral Rickover. In spite of this, the nuclear power plant was turned down by the Defense Department. This means that for thirty years or more this ship must operate with deliberately built-in obsolescence. If this is not disturbing, consider that the ship will be unable to take advantage of other progressive strides in nuclear technology which are expected in the near future.

In 1960, when it was decided to build the attack carrier USS *America* (CVA-66) with conventional power, these great advances in nuclear propulsion had not come to fruition. Futhermore, the nuclear *Enterprise* and other nuclear surface ships had not had a chance to demonstrate the overriding superiority of nuclear propulsion in fleet operations. Technological advances, as well as operational experience, favored nuclear power for the USS *John F. Kennedy*.

One little matter stood in the way of approval—cost. Yet the estimated total lifetime cost of operating a nuclear carrier with its many advantages, instead of an oil-burner, was only three per cent greater! This figure does not take into account the cost reductions in nuclear cores, certain to come before the first nuclear refueling would be required.

Attack aircraft carriers benefit from nuclear power by being able to conduct sustained operations in a combat area without refueling, and consequently can carry more aviation fuel and ammunition. Freeing carriers from the burden of refueling their escorting destroyers must await the day when the escorts are also nuclear-powered. Until then, some of the carrier's staying ability must be sacrificed.

Speaking of this problem, Capt. Vincent Paul de Poix, the first skipper of USS *Enterprise* said: "We are better off having nuclear carriers even though we must have conventional escorts, if this is the way it has to be. There are so many advantages to nuclear carriers that do not depend on escorts: maneuverability, acceleration, deceleration, absence of stack gases, ability to close ship against atomic, biological, or chemical attack.

"If you have an alert and you are steaming with conventional escorts, you could slow down to fuel those escorts and still get to your mission quicker than you could with the conventional carrier."

Capt. Eugene P. Wilkinson, the first commanding officer of USS *Long Beach*, made the following strong endorsement of the cruiser in congressional testimony: "The first propulsion plant performed just as flawlessly as that on the *Nautilus*, and showed many advantages: sustained speed, flexibility, mobility. These things are hard to measure in money. We had over a thousand officers and men on the *Long Beach*. They all knew that a nuclear power plant was better. I would have a hard time going to those men and explaining why we were getting something second rate for a little difference in money. [Referring to oil power for the *John F. Kennedy.*]

"We don't build very many of these ships. These ships are important. They are the ones with which we fight. They ought to be the best we can get."

Traditionally, destroyers have had the shortest endurance of our combatant ships when propelled by fossil fuels. The endurance limitation of a group of ships was invariably to "top off the cans"—to refuel the accompanying destroyers. At one point during the war a typhoon swept across the Pacific and made it impossible to fill the black oil bunkers of the destroyers. Unable to ballast quickly with sea water, three destroyers, riding high and light, capsized and sank in the mountainous seas. These destroyers were victims of the refueling cycle and a typhoon that would not wait. Nuclear-powered destroyer leaders cannot eliminate typhoons or hurricanes, but they can run from them, and have no stability problem resulting from a low fuel level.

Capt. R. E. Peet, the first skipper of USS *Bainbridge,* stated: "There is no question about the enthusiasm of all of us who are assigned to the *Bainbridge.* It is far and above anything else in the destroyer force. This ship is reliable, demonstrated by going over fifty to sixty thousand miles in the past year. Up to now our limit has been fuel—that is no longer a limit with the *Bainbridge.* The *Bainbridge* can steam independently any place in the world just as the carrier (*Enterprise*) could."

There are no "gas stations" at sea. The best that the Navy can do to meet this shortage is to pre-position oilers to rendezvous with other ships of the fleet. Oilers have become expert in the underway replenishment of black oil for ships' bunkers. This means planning the rendezvous, a slow-down, and possible diversion of course during pumping. It also delays a ship's arrival "on station."

Oilers are slower than combatant units, and during wartime they must be considered submarine bait, they "chum-up" the water before the arrival of the thirsty ships. Further, there is always a risk that when the ships arrive for their fuel, instead of finding the oiler, there may be nothing more than a large oil slick where it used to be. This points up the unreliability of oilers during wartime. In combat, refueling also imposes the tactical disadvantage of vulnerability because a ship is not free to maneuver if it is surprised.

Regarding the refueling problem, Vice Adm. John T. Hayward recently remarked: "If I am running at a high speed and can run continuously at this speed, even if it is a nuclear submarine, he is going to have a great deal of difficulty with me. Any time you slow down to replenish you are a 'sitting duck.' In the open sea the ability to run and run fast is one of the best protections against submarines, particularly for a combatant ship. A nuclear aircraft carrier gives you true mobility. Against submarines there is no substitute for this.

"I took the *Enterprise* to Europe and the Mediterranean. I operated under Admiral McDonald, who was Sixth Fleet Commander then. It was quite obvious to me in crossing when I had rough weather, and had the *Bainbridge* with me, that we would have been able to proceed at a great deal higher speed if we had been strictly nuclear. We lost a lot of time in fueling ships.

"The real difficulty I found was in refueling if the Atlantic Ocean was rough. The sea (at times) was so rough I could not bring the destroyers alongside to refuel them. I didn't have this difficulty with the *Bainbridge*. I would have traded eight conventional for one *Bainbridge* in the middle of the Atlantic."

A number of important advantages accrue to a nuclear ship because of the absence of smoke and stack gases. In the construction of a conventional ship, disadvantages are apparent in her design. From the boiler room of an oil-burning ship right on up through her superstructure, there is a clutter of intakes to draw in the necessary air for the insatiable fires in the firerooms. Providing oxygen for combustion is only half of the problem, however. The other is the disgorging of great volumes of exhaust gases and smoke.

These openings through the decks represent a built-in structural weakness in the overall design of a ship. They also represent an Achilles' heel of vulnerability, for severe damage to the uptakes or stacks may knock out the ship's power, even though the boilers themselves are undamaged.

Only nuclear-powered ships can be sealed in completely from atomic, biological, or chemical attack. In oil-burning ships, however, necessary openings for intakes and "smoke stacks" make it impossible to completely close the ship from outside contamination. In an age when atomic warfare and radiation contamination poses a dire threat, all conventionally-powered ships are at a disadvantage, and to some extent obsolete. Conversely, only nuclear-powered ships, both surface and submarine, can be considered fully modern.

In addition, there is the constant maintenance problem of topside equipment when it is assailed by stack gases. Radar and other electronics equipment, sprouting as they do in such abundance from the superstructures of our ships, are usually mounted high on the masts where the corrosive action of stack fumes can do the most damage. The result of this corrosion, when translated into maintenance effort, replacement parts, poorer performance, or complete failure of the equipment, is self-evident. Considering that the equipment costs millions of dollars, this round-the-clock sabotage of stack-gas corrosion results in a costly menace to the operating fleet. These funds could better be applied to the building of a nuclear ship in the first place.

Smoke from a ship's stacks is not partial only to radar masts and electronics equipment. Grimey soot from the stacks settles equally on all topside decks, ordnance gear, boats, handling-equipment, and ship's crew. Even though the Engineering Department keeps an alert watch in the fireroom to minimize black smoke, there comes a time when it is necessary to "blow tubes." This function clears the uptakes of accumulated soot for more efficient operation. To the ship's company, dressed in inspection whites, it seems like a plot by the "snipes" (anyone who stands fireroom or boiler watches) to blow tubes just before inspection. A typical remark might be: "Those blankety-blank snipes will do it every blankety-blank time." There is little doubt that the seagoing sailor will welcome the day when the "snipe" ratings associated with oil-burning systems will give way to those connected with nuclear reactors.

A sailor's fight against dirt and soot is remedied by the ship's laundry or the dry cleaners ashore. However, the shorter life of uniforms and the cost of dry cleaning is an expense that has to be borne by the seagoing man, and is of little concern to the taxpayer. What the taxpayer does pay for is the constant scraping and painting of all exterior parts of a ship due to deterioration from the chemical action of the soot, stack gases, and salt spray. The exact cost of paint deterioration could never be accurately calculated. However, a conservative guess would be measured in the millions of dollars.

Keeping ships' bunkers supplied with black oil now constitutes the major bulk of supplies required by our ships at sea. The huge fuel "pipeline" includes fuel procurement, shorebased fuel storage, pumping and control facilities, fleet oilers for underway replenishment, and on-board control in each ship. The entire complex represents one of the world's biggest logistics operations. There is a direct relationship between a ship's staying ability and her supplies. Obviously, staying ability is increased when the space saved in lieu of the huge bulk of black oil can be used for carrying ammunition, food supplies or, in the case of aircraft carriers, aviation fuel.

The record of the *Enterprise* gives every indication that she is one of the great ships of our century. Beginning with her sea trials, she steamed faster than any carrier had before, and exceeded her designed power specifications. She can keep ready power on the line, a feat which oil-burners can attain, but not sustain, over a long period.

To quote Captain de Poix: "If we were steaming at night and we had a sub contact, the standard doctrine, of course, was to get away from that contact as soon as possible. The *Enterprise* was able to accelerate to full power just by opening the throttles. It took conventional carriers a lot longer to get up to speed and, in general, they were not able to get up to full speed at all because they usually have one of their boilers down for maintenance. Because of the greater reliability of nuclear reactors, we can, and almost always do, keep the reactors on at all times."

There was convincing evidence of the superior speed, maneuverability, reliability, safety of operations, range, and staying power of a nuclear carrier. Nevertheless, the USS *John F. Kennedy* was still denied nuclear power because the cost was too high when measured by the Defense Department "cost effectiveness" calculations.

In 1963, before this decision was made, the lights burned late in the Pentagon. A group of naval officers were working on cost effectiveness studies for the Department of Defense. Their wives had been called and told not to wait dinner because they would be "a little late." They studied myriads of facts, estimates, and ideas in order to justify nuclear power for a new carrier. How much is it worth in combat to get there before the enemy expects you? How much is it worth to avoid exposing a ship to submarine attack while refueling? How much is a carrier pilot's life worth? How much is it worth to be able to remain in a strike area until the job is done, instead of leaving to refuel?

If anyone could actually supply the answers to such questions in terms of money he would have to use a crystal ball—as wondrous as nuclear power itself. It is not possible to equate safety and operational factors on a dollar basis. If life and death, or victory and defeat, are separated by a mere whisker, the arguments in favor of nuclear power have grown a full beard.

[114]

At the Pentagon, some of the cost effectiveness factors considered were:

Response time: average response differential for first, second, and third CVA to respond

Sorties: average number of sorties, at median response ranges, for first ten days after an alert

Staying power: number of consecutive days on strike stations, or the percentage of time on station over a given period

Embarked aircraft: number and type of embarked aircraft available for all types of air missions

Vulnerability: measuring the added risk associated with the refueling cycle

Task force flexibility: freedom from logistic restraints and ability for operational commander to take full advantage of deceptive tactics, weather, offensive and defensive opportunities

Readiness and reliability: adequacy of size and equipment, safety, standards of construction, and the ship as a weapons platform

Special force capability: ability of the task group to act as an "elite" force, capable of quick strike operations, or the maintenance of a militant presence in vital areas

General war capability: effectiveness of the force which could survive a nuclear exchange and retain an organized, flexible offensive capability

Other factors: advantages that accrue primarily to the nuclear group in areas of advancement of nuclear technology, ABC defense, corrosion control, island (superstructure) design, stockpiling of nuclear fuel, and potential for modernization

The Joint Committee on Atomic Energy under its chairman, Senator John O. Pastore, presented the following conclusions after a thorough investigation:

"The operations of our first three nuclear surface warships, the aircraft carrier *Enterprise,* the cruiser *Long Beach,* and the destroyer *Bainbridge,* have been an outstanding success. However, only one more nuclear-powered surface warship, authorized in 1961, is currently under construction and no more have been programmed for the future.

"On the basis of its investigation, the committee concludes that the decision announced by the Secretary of Defense on October 25, 1963, against the utilization of nuclear propulsion in the next aircraft carrier, CVA-67 [the *John F. Kennedy*], was incorrect. If this carrier, with a life expectancy of up to thirty years, is built with conventional power, it will reduce its capabilities from now until the twenty-first century.

"More tragically, such a decision means that the Navy may be committed to a future of planned obsolescence with grave implications for the national security."

Rear Adm. T. F. Connolly, who was the Director of the Strike Warfare Division in Naval Operations, ordered studies comparing the characteristics of aircraft carriers with and without nuclear power. The most important military characteristics were used in these studies, and the evaluation showed that five nuclear-powered aircraft carrier task groups would be as effective, militarily, as six new conventionally powered task groups. An even more germane argument for the cost-conscious Department of Defense was that the estimated lifetime costs of the five nuclear-powered task groups would be several billion dollars less than those of the six conventionally powered task groups.

The Admiral further pointed out: "We want very much now to stop building conventional carriers. We only have the opportunity to build a relatively few more carriers for a given period of time. One more conventional is one less nuclear."

Dr. Glenn T. Seaborg of the Atomic Energy Commission added more strength to the overwhelming argument in favor of nuclear power by saying: "We have reached a stage in the development of technology where we need to take a step toward the construction of these reactors and watch their operation. If we don't take it now, we are going to be in the position of marking time. There will be a loss of continuity in the program and a loss in the industrial capability if we stop at this stage and introduce a hiatus for an indeterminate period of time."

From his vast experience and intimate knowledge of the subject, Admiral Rickover testified before a congressional committee: "If there is one thing that is growing, it is the requirement for electrical power. If you don't have a great amount of electrical power, this ship won't be good several years from now. The important thing is to get a good (weapons) platform; get good propulsion, and get a good electrical plant because 56,000 kilowatts of electrical power is more than twice the propulsion power of the battleship *California,* just for auxiliary power. You can put that in with conventional oil, but the ship can't steam as far if you use large blocks of electrical power. You can do it with nuclear power." The Admiral also pointed out that without building nuclear ships, costs cannot be reduced—instead, they will be increased.

When Vice Admiral Hayward was the Commander of Carrier Division Two, he wrote a letter to then-Secretary of the Navy Fred Korth, in which he enthusiastically endorsed nuclear power from the operational commander's viewpoint. The letter read in part:

"I wish that others who so easily dismiss the admitted advantages of nuclear power as not being worth the cost could have shared our experience during the past two months on the Cuban blockade. It is

[117]

now even more obvious to me that the CVA-67 should have nuclear propulsion. *Enterprise* outperforms every carrier in the fleet.

"No other carrier has made over ten thousand landings in her first year of operation. Her planes are easier and cheaper to maintain and are combat ready more of the time because they are not subject to the corrosive attack of stack gases. They can fly more missions because much of the space normally used for fuel oil tankage is available for ammunition and jet fuel.

"The rugged reliability designed and built into her propulsion plant gives her a sustained high-speed and ever-ready maneuvering rate that greatly enhances air operations. The absence of boiler uptakes has allowed the arrangement of communication and radar systems superior to those on any other carrier. In Washington, these often-cited advantages of nuclear propulsion seem to get lost in a shuffle of paper—off Cuba they were real. On blockade duty our conventional escorts were usually refueled every other day. I think the Cuban crisis made all of us do a lot more thinking about how we will fare in war."

Secretary of the Navy Korth spoke out boldly in favor of nuclear power. When a man speaks with conviction and courage, regardless of the consequences, his words merit some attention:

"Within the past year, the Soviet Union has been classed officially as a major maritime power in every sense except surface striking power. By 1970, their merchant fleet will exceed our own. They are taking to the sea out of military and mercantile necessity, and it is at sea that they will at last become vulnerable to the traditional interest and influence of the Western Allies—all of whom are essentially maritime in nature, and largely dependent upon American sea power for backbone.

"The basic question now before us is simple: Will we meet the future challenges at sea with modern, high-speed, nuclear-powered surface forces, or will we continue the shortsighted, budgetary ex-

[118]

pedient of hamstringing our new ships—already too few in number—with obsolete engines?"

Senator Pastore pointedly remarked: "The fact of the matter is that a nation that gives four billion a year in foreign aid can't afford to give the Navy the best kind of ship." The answer is simple enough: foreign aid does not have to meet cost effectiveness standards.

As a conventionally powered ship, the new attack aircraft carrier *John F. Kennedy* will never be fully in step with the free-wheeling mobility required of the more forward strategy, imposed by the diverse and distant trouble spots of the world. She will always be hobbled by the restrictive black-oil hose needed to fill her fuel bunkers.

In every other aspect, however, the carrier will be in step with our latest technology. This fine ship will have the new high capacity communications system (HICAP COM); twin missile launchers for long-range antiaircraft use; and the NTDS for responding quickly to a fast-moving battle situation. Her larger fuel and aviation ammunition capacity will increase her staying ability in a forward area. She will have improved radars and an automatic aircraft landing system.

In spite of her ultramodern equipment, without nuclear propulsion there will be decades of misgivings about this ship. There will be a gnawing awareness that she is not as good a ship as our country could have built—a mixture of the best and newest our technology can produce, and at the same time a step backward into the prenuclear age. We can only hope that this aircraft carrier will be the last such hybrid of the past and future.

Many of the advantages of nuclear power, when listed in logical order, appear substantial enough in peacetime. In a combat situation, when lives are at stake, all of the operational advantages seem to multiply. It is impossible to calculate how many ships were sunk during World War II after being betrayed by lingering puffs of black smoke from their stacks. A ship whose steam is heated by a nuclear reactor burns no fuel, and makes no smoke. A smoke-free, nuclear ship is harder to detect and consequently less vulnerable to attack.

The realities of world tension and conflict may, in the future, impose the supreme test of the decision to build obsolescent ships in the nuclear era. In the case of the *John F. Kennedy*, the battle between atoms and oil was lost. Each such battle lost only delays the inevitable victory of nuclear power over oil in our Navy's capital ships.

A nuclear weapon of the "Little Boy" type dropped over Hiroshima. The 9,000-pound A-bomb measured 28 inches in diameter and 120 inches in length. Navy Capt. William S. Parsons armed it in flight. (USAF)

On the ground, only a few grim landmarks of Hiroshima rise above the rubble. (National Archives)

Left: *The Naval Research Laboratory, along the banks of the Potomac, where the liquid thermal-diffusion method for isotope separation was developed.* Right: *A model plant for isotope separation, using the thermal-diffusion method.*

Operation Crossroads, July 1946. The Baker-Day bomb test at Bikini. Cloud formation at peak shortly before disintegration of mushroom shape as water column starts to fall. (U.S. Army)

Left: *Vice Admiral Hyman G. Rickover climbs up a ladder during a visit to* Nautilus. Right: *Completing a transit from the Pacific to the Atlantic under the North Polar ice pack, Cdr. William Anderson waves from* Nautilus' *bridge.*

USS Nautilus, *first atomic-powered submarine, on her initial sea trials.*

The nuclear powered submarines USS Skate *and* Seadragon *conduct exercises under the North Polar pack, and surface together at the Pole.*

World's longest submarine and the first with two nuclear reactors, USS Triton *needles through the water during sea trials. (General Dynamics)*

Capt. Edward L. Beach, *skipper of the* Triton, *plots* Triton's *position after circum-navigating the world submerged. Crossing lines of the course mark location where world-submerged trip was completed on April 25, 1960. (General Dynamics)*

First simultaneous submarine launching in history sends attack submarine Flasher *and FBM submarine* Tecumseh *down the ways into the Thames River from Electric Boat yards at Groton, Conn. (General Dynamics)*

Right: *The escape training tank with 50- and 25-foot entrance bubbles at the Naval Submarine School, New London, Conn.*

Below: *Buoyant ascent training in the escape training tank.*

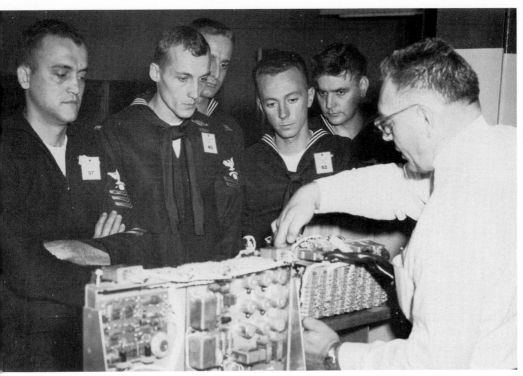

Advanced training in electronic-control-circuitry troubleshooting at the Navy Submarine School, New London.

Trainees are checked out on the high-pressure air manifold system at New London.

An off-crew from a Polaris submarine practices teamwork on an FBM Submarine Attack Center training device, New London.

A chief hospitalman demonstrates the use of radiation survey instruments to Navy nurses at the National Naval Medical Center, Bethesda, Md.

Above: *The nuclear-powered Polaris missile-firing submarine USS* Thomas Jefferson. *The tenth FBM submarine to be commissioned, she is of the* Ethan Allen *class.*

Left: *These submariners are standing watch in the control center of the USS Abraham Lincoln.*

Left: *Men of the* Nautilus *relax over a game of cards at their bunks. Each berth is equipped with a reading lamp, ventilation control, and a foam rubber mattress.* Right: *A static bicycle in USS Lafayette is one way of keeping calories under control. In background is a tape recorder for ship's entertainment system.*

Crew's mess and galley in an FBM submarine. (General Dynamics)

Built around a CVS-type aircraft carrier, this Hunter-Killer ASW Task Group includes seven escort destroyers, two submarines, and naval air support units.

Crewmen of the guided-missile destroyer USS Berkeley stand watch at the Sonar panel during fleet exercises off San Diego.

Left: *An ASROC launcher loaded and in position to fire from USS* Norfolk *during evaluation tests.* Right: *ASROC fire-control system includes a computer which processes electrical signals giving the target course and speed, wind velocity and direction, and the speed, course, pitch, and roll of the attacking ship. These signals are used to compute future position of target, launcher angle, and distance missile will fly.*

USS Keyes *fires an ASROC during ASW exercises off the California coast.*

Her twin reactors give USS Long Beach a maximum range of 720 nautical miles per day — day after day.

In addition to nuclear power, Long Beach's other modern features include fixed-array search radars and long-range missile weapons.

The in-port watch section attends Sunday services as the church flag flies at the stern of Long Beach.

Heavy seas are little problem for nuclear ships since they are free of the fueling requirement. Here Long Beach crashes into a booming sea.

Left: *The "main battery" of the giant nuclear carrier USS* Enterprise *consists of modern high-performance aircraft. Supersonic F4B Phantom IIs are spotted forward on the flight deck.*

Below: *A formation of A4 Skyhawks jet over the Nuclear Task Force during Sea Orbit, a 65-day unreplenished world cruise. In foreground is USS* Enterprise, *flanked by USS* Long Beach *(middle), and USS* Bainbridge.

New designs take form in the woodworking shop at the David Taylor Model Basin for surface ships and submarines of the future.

Closeup view of the island of the USS Enterprise. *The four rows of diagonal bars form part of the radar system of the ship.*

Above: A laboratory technician at the Naval Research
Laboratory operates master-
slave hands while working
with radioactive materials as
he observes through a 3-foot-
thick radiation-shielding window.

Left: A thick shielding door
leads into a hot cell where
work is conducted on radioactive materials at NRL.

A pool-type reactor uses fuel assemblies containing U-235 for research at NRL. The control room for the reactor can be seen in left background.

Seabees construct nuclear reactor site at McMurdo Sound to further the research effort in Antarctica.

ALVIN, *a new two-man research submarine, is about to be lowered into the water. A grappling arm in front can be used to pick up objects from the ocean bottom; to the right is one of the four viewing ports.*

SEALAB I, *an ocean station for underwater research, is a home and laboratory for aquanauts.*

Left: *Vice Admiral Rickover stands on the bridge of Te-cumseh while the command-ing officer of the Blue Crew, Cdr. A. B. Taylor, takes the conn during builder's trials.*

Below: *Navy photographers engaged in a wet job during SEALAB I operations off the coast of Bermuda in 1964.*

Right: *Technician at NNMC uses a Geiger counter to follow the circulation of radioactively tagged rabbit's blood which has been withdrawn, frozen, stored, thawed, and transfused back into the rabbit.*

Below: *At National Naval Medical Center, one hospital corpsman removes a lead-shielded bottle of Iodine-131 while another uses monitoring equipment to assure that Maximum Permissible Exposure is not exceeded.*

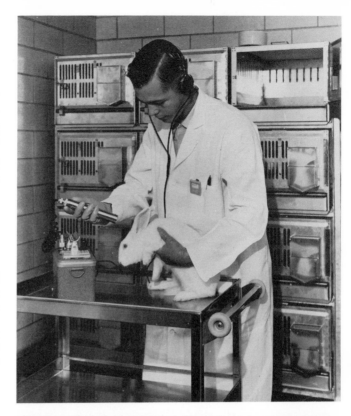

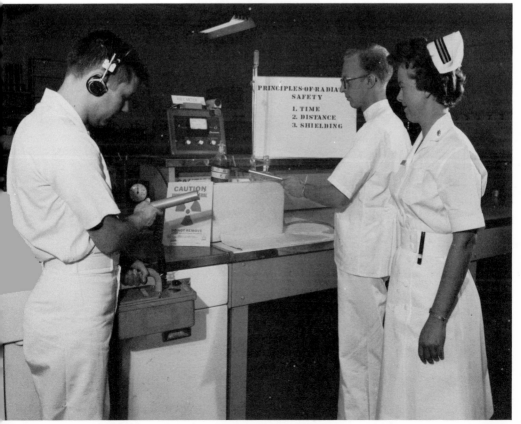

USS Kitty Hawk *gets a shower bath during an Atomic Washdown Drill at sea.*

The destroyer USS Purdy *turns on her atomic washdown system during underway training exercises.*

Three Navy carrier-type aircraft, A4Ds, are shown with Bullpup missiles slung under their fuselages.

With surface-to-air missiles on her launchers fore and aft, USS Columbus passes the tip of Point Loma as she enters San Diego Bay.

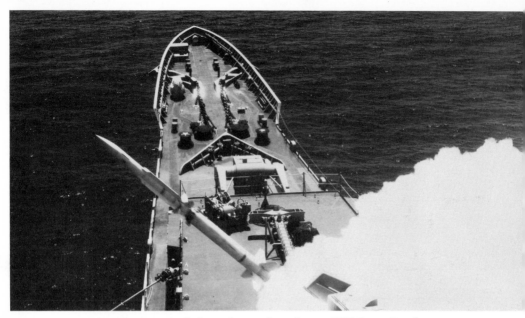

A Terrier missile leaps from a launcher on USS Long Beach.

A Talos missile in launch position on a guided-missile cruiser.

USS Halibut *unleashes a Regulus I guided missile while observers watch from the attack aircraft carrier* Lexington.

Left: *A crewman of USS* Berkeley, *a guided-missile destroyer, checks the functioning of the telemetering system receiver unit for the Tartar missile system.* Right: *An ASROC missile is loaded into a launcher on board USS* Norfolk *for evaluation tests at Key West, Fla.*

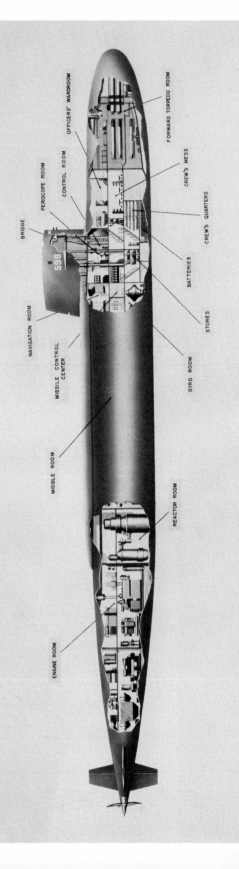

Cutaway view of a George Washington-class FBM submarine. (General Dynamics)

FORWARD TORPEDO ROOM

OFFICERS' WARDROOM

CONTROL ROOM

PERISCOPE ROOM

CREW'S MESS

CREW'S QUARTERS

BRIDGE

BATTERIES

STORES

NAVIGATION ROOM

GYRO ROOM

MISSILE CONTROL CENTER

MISSILE ROOM

REACTOR ROOM

ENGINE ROOM

598

Left: *Missilemen of the Polaris submarine USS* Lafayette *run through a missile-firing drill.* Right: *Launched from the ocean depths, a Polaris missile leaps to the surface and ignites with a terrifying roar as it climbs into the sky toward its target. It was launched from USS* Andrew Jackson.

On the surface, USS James Madison *churns through the water, while below the gradually darkening depths provide the world's greatest hiding place.*

A Star Tracker is unzipped on USS Compass Island, *the FBM navigation-development and test ship which helped perfect the accuracy of SINS (Ship's Inertial Navigation System).*

USS Observation Island, *an FBM test ship, conducted tests of the launching, fire control, and navigational devices required by the Polaris FBM system.*

Left: *One of 16 Polaris missiles is swallowed by the launching tubes of USS Abraham Lincoln.* Right: *Fifteen tons of red-dyed water is ejected from a Polaris missile tube as USS Daniel Boone tests her missile launch system.*

USS Henry Clay *launches an A-2 Polaris missile in a demonstration that submarines can launch from the surface as well as submerged.*

Left: USS Skipjack *pierces the water as her skipper, Cdr. William Behrens, puts her through her paces. (General Dynamics)* Right: USS George Washington, *the first Polaris submarine, slides down the ways of Electric Boat's "spawning ground for steel whales."*

Powered by twin nuclear reactors, USS Bainbridge *knifes through the water at high speed. Her Terrier missiles are on the launchers fore and aft.*

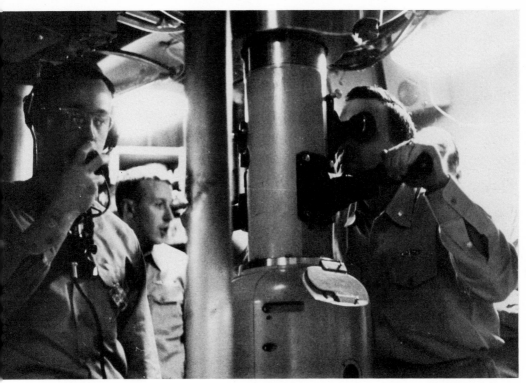

Cdr. Patrick Hannifin, skipper of USS Lafayette's Blue Crew, mans the periscope while Lt. George Long passes orders through a sound-powered phone.

Keeping an FBM submarine in trim while submerged is accomplished at the Ballast Control Panel shown on USS Patrick Henry.

Missile Compartment (center level) in USS Ethan Allen. *She launched the first A-2 Polaris missile, and also the first "live" missile with a nuclear warhead.*

ELEVEN

From Drawing Board to Shipboard

FROM THE deepest depths of the ocean to the reaches of outer space, the need to further scientific research has become increasingly vital to maintaining a position of world leadership. There is little doubt that the Navy's roles and missions involve every aspect of the sciences, and require participation in a broad cross section of commerce and industry.

Participating in virtually every activity of our modern society, the Navy is actively involved with the moon and the stars, dairy cows and coal mines, plasma physics and peanut butter, barnacles and babies, satellites and soup. Throughout this wide scope of interests, the research effort probes and pushes ideas and hypotheses to help forge a better Navy. From coast to coast, the Navy's research centers are actively working to assure that our country stays ahead in a competitive world—particularly vis-à-vis the Communist countries who are set upon the destruction of the free world.

More important than the "race for space" are the many earthbound projects whose total benefit to mankind is overwhelming. The conquest of space is important, glamorous, and new, but it is only one scientific frontier of many. It is possible that we could win the race for space, but lose the overall race for progress being waged in thousands of laboratories engaged in pure and applied science.

Our modern Navy is advancing not only on the nuclear front, but in electronics, oceanography, and many other scientific fields. A nuclear reactor does not provide navigation information, nor does it purify the air inside a submarine. A nuclear explosive does not constitute a weapons system involving control and guidance to a target. For this reason, our nuclear Navy must advance across a broad front of science and technology. Although it may be diverse, naval research and development is not haphazard. It is coordinated toward ensuring that the Navy and the Marine Corps will have the best equipment to do their jobs, and the essential knowledge to go along with them.

A great deal of the progress made through naval research and development benefits not only other components of the armed forces, but the civilian and industrial communities, as well as our allies. How the many available research facilities help to form the Navy-Marine Corps team of the next year, the next decade, and the next century, is the story of many hard-working professional people. Simply to maintain the status quo would be to fall behind in a fiercely competitive science-conscious world. Only by looking ahead today can we expect to have a completely modern Navy in the future. Our Navy of today would not have been possible without yesterday's scientific spadework.

Perhaps one of the main reasons for the modern cut of the Navy's jib is the extremely active "in-house" research program. Much research is also conducted in the laboratories of industry and universities. Other advances in scientific knowledge are in the field—down under the sea, in Antarctica, under the North Polar ice pack, or on the desert wastelands. What the Navy learns does not necessarily develop into hardware—some of the knowledge is applicable to strategy, tactics, and other operational know-how.

The Chief of Naval Operations makes known the research requirements of the operating forces through the Assistant Secretary of the Navy for Research and Development, the Office of Naval Research (ONR), and the various technical bureaus of the Navy. Looking years ahead, ONR is concerned with conceiving new ideas. Before research emerges into new types of ships, aircraft, or armament, a long process of working with principles and basic science is required to learn whether or not an idea is feasible or practical. When ONR was established in 1946, it was the first permanent government agency given the primary mission of research across the entire spectrum of the sciences.

The extensive use of the land, sea, and sky has given the Navy a scope of interest as far-reaching as the seas it must control. Research, development, test, and evaluation programs are carried out within the Navy's extensive in-house facilities, as well as by contract to industry, universities, and other organizations. Naval laboratories work primarily on matters directly connected with the needs of the operating forces. Many special naval problems are associated with the sea environment to which surface ships, submarines, and naval aircraft must be adapted. Although some of the basic research cannot be directly related to the immediate needs of the Navy, it provides a sound base of knowledge necessary to continuing progress. Research programs are coordinated and planned by ONR in collaboration with the technical bureaus, such as the Bureau of Ships, Bureau of Weapons, and Bureau of Yards and Docks.

The construction and engineering activities of the Navy under the Bureau of Yards and Docks commenced active participation in nuclear matters in the early 1950's. Although the Secretary of Defense assigned to the Army the responsibility for development of military shore-based nuclear reactors, the Navy also has a keen interest in the application and operation of shore-based plants, particularly for remote areas.

The first nuclear power plant in the Antarctic was installed with AEC-Navy cooperation at McMurdo Sound, and produced steam from its uranium core by July, 1962. This provided the McMurdo Station with electric power for heat, comfort, and operating scientific equipment. The heat generated was also used, along with oil, for for melting ice and snow to supply water. A great amount of this "frozen water" had to be hauled; to overcome this tedious job, a nuclear-powered distillation plant has been installed to convert sea water for the station's use. There is now plenty of water for drinking, cooking, and for a genuine "stateside" shower—the latter also heated by the reactor.

A Civil Engineer Corps officer is in charge of the nuclear power plant in the Antarctic. To assist him in its operation, he has eighteen Seabees, and four Hospital Corpsmen. The Corpsmen attend to the radiation safety monitoring. Although the Seabees, in the land of the penguins, usually are associated with oil drums and Sno-Cats, they now have added nuclear reactors to their "can do" repertoire.

The Seabees also employ Systems for Nuclear Auxiliary Power (SNAP) devices powered by isotopes and used as low-power energy sources for such purposes as energizing remote, unattended weather stations. One SNAP generator is used in the Antarctic at Minna Bluffs to send an automatic broadcast every six hours to McMurdo Station, giving the temperature, wind velocity and direction, and the barometric pressure. Weighing eighteen hundred and seventy pounds, the generator uses heat from forty-one thousand curies of the radioactive element strontium 90. To afford some protection from the howling, sub-zero winds, the SNAP installation is buried in the snow with an outrigger platform to keep it from settling, in case of a thaw. Only the antenna and weather sensing equipment are exposed to the elements.

A similar SNAP generator with about five times the power named "NOMAD" was installed in a weather boat during January, 1964, for use in the Gulf of Mexico. This SNAP generator, fueled by 225,000 curies of strontium 90, provides sixty watts of electrical power to transmit weather data and to operate a flashing navigational beacon on the weather boat. The work was completed by personnel of the Bureau of Yards and Docks, and the Naval Nuclear Power Unit composed of seventeen CEC officers, ninety Seabees, and twelve Hospital Corpsmen. A team from the Naval Nuclear Power Unit at Fort Belvoir, Virginia conducts periodic maintenance, and checks on the safety provisions involved in using the potentially harmful fuel elements.

Engineers and Seabees, trained in field operations required for installation of nuclear power plants and SNAP units, are expanding their skills. As they now apply the new technology of harnessing nuclear fuels, they may one day use nuclear explosives for earth-moving, and nuclear power for construction. Explosives and reactors may then become as familiar to the Seabees as is the bulldozer and the pile driver.

The U.S. Naval Ordnance Laboratory (NOL), under the Bureau of Weapons, conducts an extensive explosive research program. At White Oak, Maryland, near Washington, D.C., basic and applied research is conducted in developing weapons from their conception to the point of readiness for shipboard use. To keep ahead of current technology, NOL conducts a continuing program of basic research in aeroballistics, chemistry, mathematics, and physics.

In the process of developing sophisticated ordnance systems, NOL must pioneer in areas seldom associated with weapons. The Laboratory built wind tunnels and ballistic ranges capable of determining the drag, stability, and heating effects of projectiles at velocities approximately eighteen times the speed of sound. This was directly applicable to the growth of a whole family of missiles. However, in the process, the Laboratory discovered seven new magnetic materials for use throughout the government and industry.

The high velocity weapons tests required the creation of a new high-speed tracking camera to record flight characteristics. In advancing the technology of photo instrumentation, NOL's engineers devised an ultra high-speed camera capable of recording exposures down to one-fiftieth of a millionth of a second!

Many of the scientific and engineering advances led to a great variety of contributions in many fields. To improve the switches for arming and fuzing mechanisms used in nuclear and high explosive weapons, new techniques were developed to substantially increase the strength of welded connections in fine wire circuitry. Shock testing devices, required but unavailable, had to be invented and built. Having created the world's largest shock tester, NOL also devised a hand-held "shocker" weighing only six pounds, which has been useful in checking out instrumentation in weapons.

Whatever the atmospheric conditions a weapon is called upon to endure, NOL can duplicate to pre-test the weapon's components before it is completed. An Environment Simulation Laboratory puts a weapon under extremes of temperature, humidity, pressure, vibration, and acceleration. Materials research develops new magnetic and plastic materials for weapon components. The projectiles are given "flight tests" in hypersonic wind tunnels and ballistic ranges, with advanced mathematics assisting in predictable areas of behavior, using digital and analog computers. From the scientific cornucopia of basic and applied research, come improvements in propellants, explosives, lasers, materials, and oceanography.

Oceanography is of particular interest at NOL, the Navy's primary developer of underwater and ASW ordnance. One of the interesting sound experiments under the sea was recording a shot heard half-way around the world. Research explosives dropped in the South Atlantic and the Indian oceans, and from as far away as Perth, Australia, were recorded in Bermuda. The explosives were detonated at sixty-six selected positions to collect data for improving sonar and underwater communications.

One of the spectacular devices used in the measurement of sound transmission and propagation through water is the Seagoing Platform for Acoustic Research (SPAR). A cylindrical vessel, three hundred and fifty-four feet long, SPAR is towed to any desired spot in the ocean, and changed to a vertical position by shifting ballast, and flooding. As a stable instrumentation platform, SPAR transmits precise underwater sound information by cable to a nearby control ship from acoustic signals ranging from five to one hundred miles.

A similar oceanographic experimental device, built on the West

Coast under ONR, is FLIP, a cylinder about three hundred and fifty feet long, varying in diameter from twenty feet to twelve feet. Towed to sea horizontally, it is flooded down to "flip" into a vertical position. At the top are two laboratories, living quarters, and machinery spaces. Its purpose is to provide a stable platform for very accurate acoustic and electromagnetic measurements at predetermined sea locations.

H. A. Perry, a research materials engineer at NOL, has developed a strong, transparent material to overcome the semi-blindness of undersea research vessels—glass. Resembling a huge camera lens, these windows on the undersea world acquired greatly increased strength and pliancy. A plastic overlay gives additional resistance to damage, and strength tests showed the material's greater ability to withstand shock pressures as the depth increased. Submerging to twenty-one thousand feet, experiments confirmed that the new-found ruggedness of glass windows promise to give us a much better look at our fascinating underwater world.

Oceanography, although it is practically in its infancy, is vitally important to the operation of our nuclear submarines on a global scale. Fuller exploitation of the three dimensions of the seas is necessary to modern naval warfare. Oceanographic research vehicles, resembling flying saucers with large "bug-eyed" ports for viewing, can significantly further our awakening interest in oceanography.

A number of deep-diving vehicles are emerging to advance our underwater research. *Alvin,* a two-man submarine with a cruising speed of two-and-a-half knots for eight hours, is able to attain depths down to six thousand feet. Twenty feet long, and equipped with four ports for observation, *Alvin* will be useful in exploring the ocean bottom along the continental shelf.

Another deep-sea vehicle is the submarine *Dolphin,* which is used to gather information needed for the design of deeper diving submarines for the fleet. The *Dolphin* will make new use of plastic parts in developing hull structures, and will provide information on the

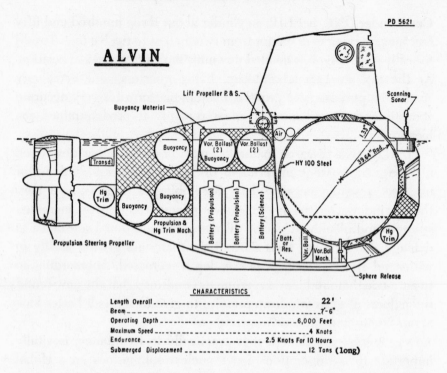

ALVIN

PD 5621

CHARACTERISTICS	
Length Overall	22'
Beam	7'-6"
Operating Depth	6,000 Feet
Maximum Speed	4 Knots
Endurance	2.5 Knots For 10 Hours
Submerged Displacement	12 Tons (long)

problems of deep-water sonars, weapons, and tactics for the deeper-diving, quieter-running submarines of the future.

The interest of industry in underwater exploitation has led to the construction of the *Aluminaut,* an aluminum submarine built by the Reynolds Metals Company. The virtually untapped wealth of the seas is expected to attract further ventures into exploring the resources locked in the depths.

One of the most famous of the deep-divers is the bathyscaphe *Trieste,* which has a round pressure hull for the two-man crew, supported by an upper hull filled with gasoline for flotation and buoyancy. Operated by the Naval Electronics Laboratory (NEL) near San Diego, the *Trieste* already has reached the deepest spot in the oceans. In January, 1960, she descended 35,800 feet to the bottom of the Marianas Trench, near Guam. After a thorough overhaul, she was later used in the Atlantic to search for evidence following the loss of the submarine *Thresher*.

Located on a high promontory of land at Point Loma, NEL, under the technical direction of Dr. Ralph Christensen, has a scientific staff of seven hundred and fifty people. Their efforts, divided into three broad categories, are in undersea technology, electromagnetics technology, and data systems and evaluation. Working under the Bureau of Ships, NEL is responsible for research and development of electronics, and related fields of engineering and science. This includes radio, radar, sonar, and oceanography as they relate to our operating Navy, and all shipboard electronic systems except those used in weapons fire control.

The Naval Tactical Data System used in a number of our large combatant ships was developed at NEL. Also built at the Laboratory was the Naval Electronic Warfare Simulator (NEWS). Installed at the Naval War College at Newport, Rhode Island, NEWS provides advanced training to officers of the armed forces in reacting to an infinite number of war situations. This is useful in nuclear as well as conventional warfare training on the command level.

Other notable NEL achievements include a new flight deck communications system, a meteor-burst communication technique for fast transmission and reception of messages, a long-range navigation system (OMEGA) using very low-frequency radio techniques, and new aspects of oceanographic research using a number of specially equipped research ships.

Of great interest is the work in underwater phenomena, and submarine environmental research. Submarines exploring under the North Polar ice pack used iceberg detection sonar, and other electronic and mechanical equipment developed at NEL, which were important to the success of these voyages. The electronic equipment helped our nuclear submarines to avoid downward-reaching ice, and assisted in locating the polynyas in the ice through which the submarines might surface. One of the world's leading sea-ice physicists from NEL, Dr. Waldo K. Lyon, accompanied the *Nautilus* on the first cruise under the North Pole.

Capt. George Bond, an expert in submarine medicine, conducted important experimentation in living underwater with a project called "Sealab" during the summer of 1964. Serving as home and laboratory, Sealab was sunk in the ocean off Bermuda, where Navy divers and their piscatorial neighbors observed each other with mutual curiosity. Serviced by an umbilical cable from the surface, the tube-like steel Sealab, forty feet long by ten feet in diameter, was open to the sea at the bottom for access, and to maintain the same pressure as the water depth.

Breathing a mixture of eighty per cent helium, sixteen per cent nitrogen, and four per cent oxygen, the aquanauts lived one hundred and ninety-two feet under the sea for eleven days, observing and gathering marine specimens for study. This was a bold venture in adapting man to the ocean depths which await his exploitation.

The expansion of the United States' efforts in marine laboratories is a step in the right direction. TENOC, a billion-dollar, ten-year program in oceanography, is one in which all the maritime nations of the world have an interest. It is quite possible that relatively poor nations with an active program in oceanography might advance economically far beyond the scope of their land resources. This could be accomplished during an era when leading nations perhaps are expending a disproportionate amount of money on outer-space research. "The pot of gold at the end of the rainbow" might be under the seas—and it wouldn't have to be hauled so far!

Progress is seldom accidental; it must be continuing and directed. Building better ships, aircraft, and submarines has been the main job of the David Taylor Model Basin (DTMB) for over fifty years— ever since its beginning in 1914. The DTMB now located in the Potomac River Valley upriver from Washington, built the first model basin, and the first wind tunnel in the United States. Gaining rapid leadership in naval architecture, DTMB designed the hull of the

Navy-Curtiss flying boat that made the first transatlantic crossing.

Advanced work at DTMB in hydronamics, aerodynamics, structural mechanics, applied mathematics, and acoustics and vibration continues to make solid contributions to the better ships and planes of the future. As nuclear power, higher speeds, and deeper diving submarines demand tougher hulls of better design, the Model Basin is also pushing forward in greater propulsion efficiency, hydrofoil craft, planing catamarans, hydro-skis, supercavitating hydrofoils, and air-cushion vehicles. Here, the shape of the future is under development today.

The all-purpose, do-everything fighting machine has always been a long-standing joke, and the subject of many Rube Goldberg-type cartoons. Most of them were flying machines which could operate under the water, as well as roll along the ground. But the time has passed for joking about such an omni-purpose device. In November, 1964, the Navy awarded a contract for analytical design studies for a flying submarine to the Convair and Electric Boat Divisions of General Dynamics Corporation.

This does not mean that the idea for such a fantastic vehicle will soon produce operational models, piloted by naval officers with golden wings and twin dolphins pinned over their coat pockets. But it does show how advanced our thinking has become. Between industrial and in-house research, the Navy may just pull this one "out of the hat."

The idea of establishing a research organization within the Navy proper came from no less an authority on inventions than Thomas A. Edison. In an article published in July, 1915 in the *New York Times Magazine,* he expressed the opinion that "the Navy should have its own scientific staff to sift the ideas of our inventive nation. It should have its own laboratory, indigenous to the Naval Establishment, in which the ideas or inventions could be tested and adapted to the peculiar needs of the Fleet."

Struck with this idea, Secretary of the Navy Josephus Daniels wrote a letter to Edison, requesting him to form a technical advisory group of leading scientists and engineers. Twenty-four men were selected—the most prominent in their fields—and they formed a "brain trust" known as the Naval Consulting Board of the United States. Their primary purpose was to screen the hundreds of inventions submitted to the Navy Department in order to weed out the impractical and crackpot from the worthwhile.

As one of its first matters of business, the Board drew up a proposal and plan for a research laboratory. The ensuing Naval Appropriations Act of 1916 provided money for "laboratory and research work on the subject of gun erosion, torpedo motive power, the gyroscope, submarine guns, protection against submarines, torpedo and mine attack, improvement in submarine attachments, improvement and development in submarine engines, storage batteries and propulsion, aeroplanes and aircraft improvement in radio installations, and such other necessary work."

A million dollars was appropriated in the budget for the fiscal year 1917. However, at this time, although the sentence structure may have been rather long, time was short for research. World War I was about to engulf the United States and many of its ambitious plans, including the laboratory. However, after the war, the Naval Research Laboratory was finally built and dedicated in July, 1923.

The rural setting of the original laboratory, which was accessible only by a dirt road, bore little resemblance to the sophisticated establishment now sprawling along the banks of the Potomac. The original laboratory is difficult to find among the present complex of buildings where over three thousand people work to support approximately four hundred concurrent projects. Some of the facilities are at nearby sites, such as the radar-astronomy complex at Stump Neck, Maryland; the Maryland Point Observatory; and the NRL Chesapeake Bay Annex for experimental work on radars. Much research work is done in places outside of the laboratory—in the Sahara

Desert, on the high seas, under the ocean, and in the upper atmosphere.

One of NLR's highlights of accomplishment was the invention of radar in March, 1934, following its use of radio pulses for detection of ships and aircraft. Radar was rivaled in importance by the improved air and surface radio communications, and underwater sound equipment. These monumental developments alone would have fully justified the Navy's in-house research establishment.

NRL was often relied upon to provide "inventions on demand," and added immeasurably to the effectiveness of the Fleet during World War II. There was little time to think about the origin of the equipment used in ships of the fast carrier Task Force 58. One of these was the Plan Position Indicator (PPI scope)—a calibrated radar scope, dimly illuminated with colored lights that showed little "blips," indicating the positions of nearby ships. A hand rotates around and around on the PPI to reinforce the impressions with each sweep. During the darkest nights, the blacked-out ships maintained their positions by using the PPI scopes, as dozens of officers of the deck peered into the glowing radar dials. No thought was given to where the radars came from; the important fact was that they were there to "see," when eyes could not.

When the Combat Air Patrol (CAP) flew over the Task Group to guard against the approach of enemy planes, the ship's radio could pick up the pilot's electrifying message, "Bandits over the Task Group." The radio communication was possible, from air-to-surface and from ship-to-ship, through the research carried out at NRL. To the operating fleet, radios, radars, and sonars were important tools of naval warfare which were mere ideas twenty years before.

Since World War II, NRL has added new dimensions to its research endeavors. These include the areas of upper atmosphere research, earth satellites and satellite detection systems, radio astronomy, thermonuclear reactions, and advanced electronics. Since

[133]

its origin, the Laboratory has expanded to thirteen research divisions: Applications Research, Atmosphere and Astrophysics, Chemistry, Electronics, Mechanics, Metallurgy, Nucleonics, Optics, Radio, Radar, Radiation, Solid State Physics, and Sound.

To cover all of the significant research projects in progress at NRL would fill a book itself. However, the highlights of achievement in the Nucleonics and Radiation Divisions are of special interest in connection with our nuclear Navy. As mentioned in a previous chapter, NRL was the first government organization to begin research in atomic energy, having developed a method for uranium isotope separation.

Because of its forward looking inquisitiveness, NRL was bound to get involved with our first atomic explosions, as well as the first Russian atomic bomb test in 1949. The year before, a group at the Laboratory had placed some gamma ray counters on the roof of one of the buildings to see what radioactivity might be gathered in. It was similar to a "fishing trip." They soon noticed that the gamma activity went up sharply every time it rained. This proved that the falling rain was scavenging radioactivity from the air. It was not then known whether this was normally in the atmosphere, or whether it was fallout from nuclear explosions.

The group of scientists working under Dr. Peter King at NRL decided to investigate the possibilities of collecting rainwater at distant places to discover what could be learned about the detection of atomic explosions. It was hoped that the evidence would tell when an explosion took place, what kind of fissionable material had been used, and perhaps something about the efficiency of the explosion itself.

Urgently needed was old rainwater, to be collected from various locations around the globe. One of the naval officers recalled that rainwater was saved and used in the Virgin Islands, and that it might be possible to find a cistern which had not been disturbed for a few months.

In a short time, one of the men was on his way with an unusual mission. He was to scrounge a tank truck and pump from the Chemical Corps, find a reservoir with some old water, fill up the tank with about twenty-five hundred gallons, treat it with chemicals, throw the water away, and come home with the material that had settled to the bottom.

Mission accomplished, the group at NRL went through a process of chemical separation of the Virgin Islands water residue, and then placed it under a Geiger counter. To their great surprise, they found fission activity—and spent the next several months trying to prove that their findings were wrong. However, Dr. King's group was forced to conclude that they were right. The "junk" they were working with proved to be debris from a bomb explosion nine thousand miles away!

This was the first step toward more extensive rainwater sampling in various parts of the world. Among the remote spots chosen were Shemya, the last island in the Aleutian chain; Kodiak, Alaska; and Truk Island. Puddles, old wells, anything that contained rainwater samples would do. At Moem, near Truk Island, John Kane from the NRL group found an abandoned swimming pool, apparently used by the Japanese in World War II as an officer's rest camp. In gathering this old water, Kane also found a mossy growth around the edge of the pool which he tore off, and sent back to the Laboratory in an old paint can. Both were tested. The amounts of radioactivity were useful as a basis against which to compare later samplings.

One unusual experiment took place right on the grounds of the Naval Research Laboratory. As Dr. King said: "I had the experience of telling a rather hard-boiled foreman, in charge of a group of laborers, that I wanted about a dozen men to go up on the roof of that building over there—scrub the roof, using new brushes, and save all the wash water. He looked at me as though I were crazy, and repeated incredulously, 'scrub the roof?' He had been around for twenty-five years, and had been asked to do a lot of silly things for scientists around the place, but 'this was the first time he had been asked to wash a roof.' However, if I wanted it washed, he would wash it.''

The rainwater sampling method of identifying fallout from atomic bombs paid big dividends. About five stations from Japan to Africa were selected to collect rainwater, and filter radioactivity from the air. At each station, the air was pulled through a filter with a blower. Whenever the activity on the filter paper reacted in a peculiar manner, the very next rain was to be sampled, and the residue from it quickly flown back to NRL.

After months of negative readings, the Kodiak station came through with a dispatch in September, 1949, that indicated unusual activity. The available water was treated and rushed back to Washington by plane, via a fast relay through Seattle.

Arriving at 4:00 A.M., the pilot was curious as to "why in the world we had to go all the way to Kodiak for three gallon jugs of junk?" Since the information was then restricted to "need-to-know" basis, the pilot may still not know the answer to his question.

Perhaps even more difficult for the NRL group was trying to answer the questions of wives who were justifiably curious about their husbands arriving home between two and five A.M. Not until about two years after the long-suffering husbands simply told their wives that they were "at work," could they explain the strange "goings on" in the middle of the night with the jugs of "junk."

When the Kodiak "slush" was processed, it was found to have hundreds of thousands of counts per minute of fission products. We then knew for certain that the Soviet Union had successfully exploded an atomic bomb. Up to this time, air monitoring had shown relatively small variations in radioactivity, but this evidence was overwhelming. Improved methods of detection have since been developed, and other agencies have taken up the monitoring business.

The following programs show in part the wide diversification of scientific research at NRL: study of ferrous alloys; shock and vibration; nuclear reactions in the sun; self-luminous sources of light; determination of universal constants of physics; interference-free communications channels; oceanographic research; extreme temperature lubricants; portable automatic weather stations; space cartography; microanalysis of metals and alloys; and ultraviolet laser beams.

While work on Polaris missiles and bouncing messages from the moon are directly applicable to the Navy's needs, basic research on other projects are also of great interest. The Vanguard program, which resulted in a satellite being placed in orbit by the United States in March, 1958, was designed and the satellite built at NRL. It is still up there, with its solar-powered radio transmitting. Much of the technology developed for Vanguard is still being applied in our satellite programs, now under NASA. Many of the basic research projects, although developed under the Navy's aegis, are passed on to other government agencies.

NRL acquired a nuclear reactor for research, and in September, 1956 brought it critical for the first time. This opened up a new line of investigation in the physical sciences by providing a source of neutrons and gamma rays for research programs. The neutrons produced are used to study the structure of matter and new alloys, produce new substances, and make them radioactive for study.

Gamma rays emitted by the reactor operating at one thousand kilowatts (its licensed power rating) are approximately ten million curies. These emissions are equivalent to that of ten tons of radium. This controlled source of gamma radiation is useful in studies on shielding and radiation damage.

The NRL reactor is a pool-type; its fissionable material (U-235) being immersed in a pool of specially treated water of high purity. The water slows down the fast neutrons from about ten thousand miles per second to one mile per second. This reduces the amount of U-235 required to sustain a nuclear chain reaction, since the slow-moving neutrons are the ones relied upon to continue splitting the nuclei of U-235 to yield more neutrons. Water also serves as a coolant to remove heat from the fuel assemblies, and provides shielding to protect personnel from the harmful neutron and gamma rays. The 150,000 gallons of water in the pool may be drained into an underground tank where it is carefully analyzed to make sure that it is below the Atomic Energy Commission's tolerance levels before it is discharged into the Potomac River.

The remote control safety features are of special interest since they are widely adopted in other laboratories. The reactor is operated from a console in the control room, providing distance and shielding from the "hot" areas. Small quantities of materials to be irradiated are slipped into little containers called "rabbits," and popped into pneumatic tubes. After exposure, they are returned to lead-lined containers outside the shielded area, or sent directly to remote receivers nearby.

Hot material can be handled by remote-control, master-slave manipulators, while the operator stands behind a radiation-shielded protective window. These windows are three feet thick, with one-inch-thick plate glass on either side, and the intervening space filled with a dense liquid (a saturated solution of zinc bromide) having good optical properties.

One of the fascinating nuclear and radiation research tools at NRL is an electron linear accelerator (LINAC). Installed in 1963, LINAC replaced the twenty-two-million-volt betatron, and produces an electron beam having an intensity five thousand times greater. LINAC can accelerate electrons in evacuated tubing to strike a target at a velocity approaching the speed of light—186,000 miles per second. Used for basic research in nuclear physics, LINAC is also used for studies in intense radiation.

Secondary beams of X rays, positrons, and neutrons are used for numerous experiments. X rays produce radioisotopes which are usually different from those produced by the neutrons in the pool-type reactor. LINAC in this manner complements the experiments in the reactor by providing a more complete representation of the many radioisotopes. A safety feature of LINAC is the shielding by seven-foot-thick concrete walls, in addition to radiation monitoring devices.

Since the Navy is one of the world's largest users of power, new sources of power are of special interest in naval research. In recent years, one of the sources explored was the "harnessing" of bugs. This may conjure up a picture of an array of tiny insects, harnessed together with spider-web-thin lines, perhaps towing a four-wheeled peanut shell. However, the "bugs" in question are microscopic bacteria present in sea water which can be developed into a colony of bacteria. When such a colony adheres to the surface of a steel plate, it can be used as a cathode for a sea-water battery. The resultant power, however small, would generate a reliable and lasting source of electricity to provide buoys with audible, visual, or radio signals. The sea-water battery would have numerous applications for remote oceanographic instruments, or even for antisubmarine monitoring beacons.

Thinking small is often as necessary as thinking big. Scientists at NRL are interested in extracting power from these microscopic bacteria, as well as in using the basic energy source of the sun and the stars. This energy is the result of fusion of the lightest of the elements, hydrogen.

The two heavier isotopes of hydrogen, deuterium and tritium, promise to give up more energy than that required to bring about a controlled thermonuclear reaction (CTR). It is possible now to extract energy from fusion by an uncontrolled thermonuclear hydrogen bomb. Its utility admittedly is severely limited when the hydrogen fusion reaction expends its energy in a fraction of a microsecond, and blasts a man out of his socks if he should happen to be anywhere near the neighborhood of a thermonuclear blast.

Under laboratory conditions, fusion reactions can also be produced. However, the energy expended in producing such a reaction is far greater than that extracted from the hydrogen isotopes. The nuclei of deuterium (deuterons) can be accelerated in a cyclotron apparatus and smacked at tremendous speeds into a solid mass containing deuterium or tritium. A fusion reaction results with the release of energy. Unfortunately, it is only a fraction of the energy required to attain the high acceleration of the deuterons. This might be compared with running up a ladder with a bucket of water to turn a mill wheel, when it would be less exerting to turn the wheel by hand.

There is probably no scientific project in progress today that is more exciting and promising to mankind than developing a successful CTR. The AEC is working on this possibility; it is called "Project Sherwood," and a number of research efforts are being pursued in a cooperative effort. One of the projects is now being conducted at NRL under Dr. W. C. Hall, the Associate Director of Research for Nucleonics, and Dr. A. C. Kolb, who has become eminent in the international community of plasma physicists.

Tapping this inexhaustible source of energy would have a profound effect on the world. Dr. Kolb pointed out: "We could work for fifty years in vigorous, costly research, and still find controlled thermonuclear energy an outstanding bargain. The problem today is to determine whether or not it is possible in principle to build a reactor. This involves the basic investigation of the physics of high-temperature, ionized gases—that is a plasma."

Although mentioning nothing of his own substantial contribution toward making that goal a reality, Dr. Kolb said that solving the problems of attaining a CTR will not be the work of one man, one organization, or one country. However, the nation which first succeeds in unlocking this vast, inexpensive source of power will realize an important advantage among nations—economic, political, and psychological. Its implications in supplying a cheap source of water, space propulsion, and industrial power are some of the exciting possibilities.

The raw materials used would probably be sea water and lithium materials, which are abundantly available all over the globe. It is calculated that the nuclear fusion energy available in each gallon of sea water would equal the energy output from more than three hundred gallons of gasoline! With most of the earth covered with sea water, the energy represented could be the greatest bounty of wealth that man has ever acquired. Imagine a ship of the Navy propelled by a CTR power plant, steaming through an inexhaustible ocean of "fuel"!

Fusion energy has a greater advantage of safety over fission reactors in that there is not a major problem in accumulating large amounts of radioactive waste material, as is the case with fission reactors. However, there would be a necessity for heavy shielding to avoid the escape of neutrons and other harmful emissions during the power plant operation. A great deal of energy (or a high temperature) is required to effect a forceful enough collision of the nuclei involved to overcome the powerful electrostatic forces which hold them apart. To do this would require elaborate, expensive, and powerful equipment in order to generate plasma temperatures over one hundred million degrees centigrade.

The plasma physics laboratory at NRL has been working on thermonuclear fusion research since 1957. One of the remarkable pieces of equipment used was the largest electromagnet in the world at that time. The electrical power used for heating the deuterium into a plasma state is provided by a large bank of condensers which store enough energy to provide fifteen million amperes of current. Power shot into the gas discharge builds up to about one hundred thousand megawatts—approaching the total electrical power used in the United States at any one moment. The charge of electricity surges through the electromagnet to produce high magnetic fields and compress the deuterium gas into a thin line of plasma heated to multimillion-degree temperatures. In about thirty microseconds the event is over, but not before spectrographs and high-speed cameras have recorded the findings for study.

On the outside of the enclosure where all of this takes place, a heavy steel mesh net covers the concrete block construction. This foreboding safety measure was not erected because a thermonuclear reaction might "rearrange" the wall—it was a precaution to protect personnel in case the huge charge of electricity, used to produce the reaction, accidentally short-circuited and caused an unwanted explosion. This is without a doubt one of the most exciting single scientific projects on earth.

The industrial revolution of the last century helped to make our country great, and provided the United States with the highest standard of living among the major powers on earth. Today we are involved in a scientific revolution, with the promise of far greater benefits to our nation. Without the restless progress from drawing board to shipboard, our Navy today could not be as effective in helping to preserve the peace in the widely scattered trouble spots of the globe.

TWELVE

Health and Safety

FROM THE beginning of time, every new form of power or energy has produced along with it dangers capable of killing or inflicting injury. Steam-heated boilers pose the dangers of fire and live steam. Electricity can cause fires through faulty wiring, or death by electrocution. Gasoline engines throw off carbon monoxide poison. By pushing down on the accelerator of a gasoline engine, over 47,000 people were killed on the highways in the United States during 1964, and over one-and-a-half million were injured! Needless to say, the dangers of nuclear power were demonstrated to a shocked world with the disastrous explosions over Hiroshima and Nagasaki.

It is to the credit of the Atomic Energy Commission, American industry, and the U.S. Navy (the largest user of nuclear energy) that there have been no incidents of death or injury in the operation of naval nuclear reactors.

In a letter to Secretary of the Navy Korth dated January 29, 1962, Glenn T. Seaborg, Chairman of the Atomic Energy Commission, wrote in part: "I want to assure you that any credit given to this Commission concerning the public health and safety aspects of the nuclear Navy should be shared with the Navy Department. We believe that cooperative efforts of the Navy and of this agency, throughout the history of the program, have resulted in a high degree of protection not only to the public, but also to operating personnel.

"You may not be aware of the excellent relationship which exists between our two organizations. The arrangement established several years ago of having a central point, or joint AEC-Navy office, has worked very well under the capable direction of Admiral Rickover."

This remarkable safety record has been established and maintained from the time that the first naval reactor went critical at Arco, Idaho. The Navy has operated many more reactors than the total of all other nuclear reactors in the world. Rather than become complacent with this perfect safety record, Admiral Rickover vigorously pursues every conceivable facet of the safety program with a zeal that is contagious, from reactor design through training and operation.

Captain de Poix told the members of the Joint Committee on Atomic Energy during a visit to the *Enterprise:* "The very thorough and extensive personnel training program which has been extant for several years of the naval nuclear propulsion program is excellent, and I think it produces real dividends in the operation of the ships as well as in the safety of the reactors. We feel that operationally it is much safer and also produces a more reliable plant if your operators are sufficiently knowledgeable and well-enough trained so you don't have to depend on the mechanical safeguards."

When asked in Congressional testimony to indicate the important factors in maintaining such an outstanding safety record, Admiral Rickover replied: "The first factor is to have people in charge who are thoroughly competent in the design and operation of reactors, both the scientific and engineering aspects—people who follow the work every minute of the day and night and do not depend on anyone else to do the work for them.

"The second factor is the acceptance of personal responsibility—to carry out your responsibility, you must select and train the people and check on the operation of the ships. You must check on the design, make sure of the excellence of the laboratories doing the work, see to it that the industrial organizations manufacturing the individual items are doing their job right, and prepare new specifications as necessary. You must be personally and emotionally involved in every single feature of the program. Otherwise, you will inevitably run into trouble.

"The Navy permits me to interview every officer who enters the program and to make recommendations to the Chief of Naval Personnel. Those selected, both officers and men, are given an intensive course of training. All of the men must learn the theory and the practical details of operating a nuclear power plant. But the education and training does not stop there, because after they are assigned to a ship they must continue to learn.

"About a month before a reactor is ready to go critical, a group of my senior people and I spend two days examining the officers and men in the engineering department—about half the crew—to ascertain whether they are fully qualified. This examination is very strict. If the crew is found to be qualified, they are authorized to bring the reactor critical. If we find them not qualified, we indicate the areas of weakness and the additional work they must do, and we reexamine them later.

"Whenever one of our new types of plants is ready to go critical, we notify the Licensing and Regulation Division of the AEC. We also notify the Reactor Safeguards Committee, and we have these two groups evaluate our design and operating procedures. No ship goes to sea without having had such an investigation."

Admiral Rickover is in charge of the first sea trials of every nuclear ship. He and senior members of the Naval Reactors Branch are responsible for conducting the propulsion-plant trials of each new ship.

The care and conservatism built into naval reactors was such that, commencing with *Nautilus*, exposure of operating personnel to radiation was harmless and well below AEC radiation standards. Although a man is permitted twelve rems—radiation dosage equal to one roentgen of X ray—in any one year (as long as it does not exceed five times his age minus eighteen), the reactor shielding in the Navy's ships is designed for five rems per year. By actual records, the men who worked in the engineering department of nuclear submarines received only one-half rem, and the highest recorded doses were only one or two rems per year.

The levels of radioactivity in the submarines are so low that they are barely within the limits of the radiation monitoring equipment. Chief Hospital Corpsman R. W. Gilbreth, who served in the Polaris submarine *Thomas Jefferson,* and worked closely with radiation monitoring, claimed that he was exposed to more radiation while at home than during patrols.

Since Admiral Rickover is personally involved in safety procedures where naval reactors are concerned, he speaks with unique authority: "Our attitude is that we will not unnecessarily take a risk, even a remote one. We design the utmost safety into them. We review the design and fabrication in detail. We have the responsibility to assure the public we are not taking any unnecessary or unreasonable risks. We are trying to establish criteria and experience that will indicate to the public, and that they will gradually accept, that nuclear submarines are safe."

Much concern is shown all over the world regarding the amount of radioactive waste discharged overboard in ports where nuclear ships call. The water permitted to be discharged into harbors, as agreed upon by the Navy, AEC, and the Public Health Service, contains many times less radioactivity than the drinking water tolerances defined in the National Bureau of Standards handbooks.

With the many nuclear submarines operating in and out of the New London/Groton area, the radioactivity has been amazingly low. Admiral Rickover has stated: "The amount of radioactivity we have discharged into New London harbor has been checked by the local authorities, by the Connecticut State Department of Health, and by the U.S. Public Health Service, and it is well within drinking water tolerance. We have never had a case when it has been otherwise."

It is a practice to discharge water into a harbor when a nuclear reactor is brought critical for warm-up. The radioactivity of this water is so low that it cannot be detected, even next to the ship. It is probable that after the discharge, a measurable quantity of water in a harbor would be no more radioactive than before. It is similar to the air within a nuclear submarine. When the hatch is closed, and the submarine dives, the shielding and safety features are so excellent that the measurable radioactivity goes down when compared with the cosmic radiation in the atmosphere above the surface.

Capt. John H. Schulte, Director, Special Weapons Defense Division, Bureau of Medicine and Surgery, is a physician who has worked in submarine and nuclear medicine. He put it this way: "Submarines have proven to be the least of our worries in radiation exposure. X-ray technicians are exposed to a greater extent."

Safety has been the keynote in the nuclear weapons area, as well as in nuclear propulsion. Procedures in transporting, assembling, stowing and handling nuclear weapons emphasizes safety during every step of the way, from manufacturing to use by operational forces. Where they are used, stored, and carried, is information that is properly held only by those directly involved. This policy may be considered part of the safety-security procedure in regard to the use of nuclear weapons.

Safety measures employed by ships of the Navy include the use of decontamination lockers for Nuclear, Biological and Chemical (NBC) warfare; completely sealing ships from the outside atmosphere (possible with nuclear surface ships), and an external "washdown" system. USS *Worcester* was the first of our capital ships equipped with spray nozzles for effecting a thorough washdown of radioactive fallout which might settle on exterior surfaces.

Taking precautions is imperative for safety. However, the medical profession has a responsibility beyond safety; it must be able to apply nuclear medicine in both prevention and treatment of radiation sickness. The Navy's particular interest in radiation biology and nuclear medicine is the protection of personnel from effects of exposure to nuclear explosions, nuclear fallout, and exposure to the low levels of radiation emanating from shielded nuclear reactor compartments.

[147]

In the field of nuclear medicine and research, the Bureau of Medicine and Surgery exercises management control over a number of research activities, and sets the policy for the use of radioisotopes in all of the Navy's major hospitals. In the suburbs of the nation's capital is the National Naval Medical Center (NNMC) at Bethesda, Maryland. This is the location of a number of activities directly concerned with health and safety in the field of radiation biology and nuclear medicine.

The Naval Medical School is directly involved in research and training, and in the use of radioisotopes, for diagnosis and treatment of patients. The outstanding research work done in the tissue bank is partly accomplished through the use of various radioisotopes. This has been a revolutionary program in making it possible to have, in effect, a "spare parts" department for the human body—a truly remarkable accomplishment in the advancement of medicine and surgery.

Capt. J. H. "Smokey" Stover, Jr., Commanding Officer of the U.S. Naval Medical School, has a distinguished staff of physicians and experts in their specialties. Capt. Loy T. Brown, Chief of the Radiology Department at NNMC, has done much toward developing excellent training programs for officers and enlisted men. These courses are under the immediate supervision of Capt. Richard F. Dobbins, Director of the Department of Nuclear Medicine, who was the Medical Officer in *Nautilus* during its historic cruise under the North Polar ice pack. Comdr. John H. Ebersole, who directs the activities of the Radiation Exposure Evaluation Laboratory, was the first physician in the nuclear program, and the first ship's doctor in both *Nautilus* and *Seawolf*, our first two nuclear submarines. Capt. Royce K. Skow, Radiation Safety Officer of NNMC, has been acquiring experience in radioactivity ever since Operation Crossroads.

There are many others in the nuclear medicine training program, whose total fund of experience is priceless. This large equity in skilled and knowledgeable people is a resource of tremendous value which is hard to measure in dollars. The early participation in historical nuclear events catapulted the Navy into a position of leadership in knowledge and training, shared with thousands in the armed forces, other government agencies, and civilian scientists both in the United States and abroad.

The Naval Medical Research Institute (NMRI), also at Bethesda, conducts research projects across a broad area of special interest in the frontiers of space and aviation medicine, and in radiation protection. The results of their studies in stress physiology include man's ability to withstand exposure to extremes of hot and cold. Results are directly related to the design of protective clothing, and the construction of shelters to provide adequate protection from the effects of a nuclear attack.

At NMRI, research in biophysics includes the biological effects of radiation exposure, treatment of those injured from ionizing radiation, thermal radiation, and tolerance levels of blast effects from nuclear explosions. It is necessary to experiment with animals to determine how large a dose of irradiation over a man's entire body is dangerous, and to establish the minimum lethal dose.

The Armed Forces Radiobiology Research Institute (AFRRI) was established in 1961. Sponsored by the Defense Atomic Support Agency (DASA) as a research center for the Army, Navy, and Air Force, it is concerned with the biological effects of radiation, and their relationship to national defense. AFRRI is located on the grounds of the Naval Medical Center at Bethesda, where a cross-fertilization of ideas and experience has proven mutually beneficial. During a visit, it was noticed that ideas were exchanged between scientists from AFRRI and NNMC concerning the effectiveness of instruments and radiation safety monitoring.

Upon entering AFRRI, each person must check in at the desk to log-in, and receive his dosimeter. Before slipping it into my pocket, as one would a fountain pen, I noticed that it read thirty millirems. My escort through the laboratory and instrument spaces was the Director of Radiation Safety, Sydney Porter, Jr.

One of the central features of AFRRI is a reactor called TRIGA (derived from Training, Research, Isotope production, General Atomic). TRIGA produces repetitive, self-limiting pulses of high-energy radiations for biomedical research. With perfect safety, the TRIGA reactor can reproduce many of the effects of an instantaneous nuclear explosion, particularly on the biological effects of ionizing radiations. Of course, the blast effect is eliminated, as attested by the fact that the building is still standing on its foundation. Research is also conducted on the treatment of cancer and other diseases through laboratory-controlled amounts of nuclear energy.

Upon leaving AFRRI, I noted that my dosimeter read exactly as it did upon entering. However, I wondered about a cardboard box full of white rats with blue markings on their pink tails. Whatever hazards they endured, they looked extremely healthy for what contributions they made to the world's knowledge of radiobiology.

Providentially located on the grounds of the Naval Medical Center, AFRRI produces a variety of short-lived radioisotopes used for research in other activities of the Naval Medical Center. Within a stone's throw of AFRRI is the Navy's Radiation Exposure Evaluation Laboratory (REEL), important in the advancement of research in radiation biology and nuclear medicine. Part of their research is coordinated with AFRRI, and part of their work is in association with the tissue bank of the Naval Medical School.

One of the pioneer facilities at REEL is the whole body counter, and as the name implies, it measures the amount of radioactivity in the entire body. By scanning the body, the total degree of internal radioactive accumulation can be determined, whether exposure was acquired through ingestion, inhalation, or external exposure.

A Naval Medical Field Research Laboratory (NMFRL), located at Camp Lejeune, North Carolina, is supported by DASA, and managed by the Navy Bureau of Medicine and Surgery. Its primary purpose is directed toward developing equipment to protect personnel in the field from ionizing radiation resulting from nuclear explosions. Marine Corps personnel stationed at Camp Lejeune cooperate with the scientific staff of NMFRL in furthering the field studies.

DASA is the coordinator of Department of Defense tri-service efforts in radiation research. It fulfills the purposes of funding, avoiding duplication of effort, and disseminating findings, in order that each Surgeon General of the Army, Navy, and Air Force is able to do his job more effectively in the event of a nuclear war.

A real "early bird" in the field of radiobiology, the Naval Radiological Defense Laboratory (NRDL) has a history dating back to 1946. At that time, target ships were being returned from Operation Crossroads for decontamination at the San Francisco Naval Shipyard. The humble beginnings of the Laboratory boasted a group of five junior naval officers who had served on the radiation monitoring teams at Bikini Atoll. In the two rooms alloted to them by the shipyard, their only equipment consisted of six Geiger counters, four of which did not work, and one coffee pot which did!

This group of five faced a herculean decontamination task at a time when little was known about the hazards of nuclear aftereffects. It was natural that the organization would have to grow to meet the challenge it faced. As scientists, engineers, and laboratory technicians were added to the staff, NRDL, by late 1964, grew to approximately six hundred people, military and civilian, working in an ultramodern laboratory in San Francisco.

Among the accomplishments of NRDL are: decontamination of ships used in nuclear tests at Eniwetok; development of the ship washdown system to minimize contamination in nuclear warfare; increasing our knowledge of protective agents against radiation; and designing and testing various types of radiac equipment for monitoring. Serving as a consultant agency to the Department of Defense and other government agencies, NRDL also maintains an operational radiological control team to assist in handling nuclear accidents, should one take place.

Specialized equipment for research and analysis at NRDL and NNMC includes such items as an electron paramagnetic resonance spectrometer—"a system of electronic and microwave components for inducing and observing E-P-R signals from electron spin resonance in substances possessing a resultant electronic magnetic moment." (It is quite clear that scientists have their moments!) However, to share them with "we, the people" involves explanations in a foreign language called "scientific English." Since every branch of scientific learning has its own "dialect" in this language, John Q. Public must take for granted that the scientists are steadily making progress for the general benefit, however specialized the field of knowledge and strange the language.

⚓

THIRTEEN

Survival Under the Nuclear Mushroom

However destructive and senseless warfare may have been in the past, it has produced inspiring examples of courage and heroism. Weapons of mass annihilation are singularly inglorious, and a nuclear exchange as a means of solving international differences would mark a new high in man's inhumanity to man.

The ability to wage nuclear warfare does not render it any less repugnant to the fighting man. He is confronted with a weapon whose lethal powers include a new kind of "fire" which he cannot normally see, taste, or smell. He must, therefore, rely on supersensory instruments to determine if he is surrounded by this unseen enemy—radiation fallout. Forces engaged in combat are not as concerned about the relatively small amounts of radiation emanating from reactors and scientific equipment, as from the massive fallout, and initial nuclear radiation from the detonation of a nuclear airburst.

A most unpalatable feature of a nuclear explosion is its disastrous power, so great that it must be described in magnitudes of thousands and millions of tons of TNT igniting in a millisecond. The blast and shock of such an explosion can produce a disaster area large enough to destroy a city and its environs. Even those on the periphery of such an area are not free from contamination by radioactivity following detonation of a surface burst. It is a disturbing thought to a man who may be fighting on a distant shore, or in a ship at sea, to realize that his home town and family may not be much safer than he is from a nuclear attack.

Survival under the nuclear mushroom is complicated by three basic physical effects: blast and pressure; thermal radiation; and nuclear radiation, initial and residual. Understanding what happens in each effect may be the first step toward survival under this triple-headed monster. Naval, air, and ground forces have different problems of offense, defense, and survival. Therefore, each component of the armed forces, while having many facets of nuclear warfare in common, must develop its own peculiar doctrine, even though the hazards are fundamentally the same.

Direct-blast injuries from a nuclear explosion are caused by the high pressure which engulfs the body, and causes rapid compression and decompression. As this pressure is transmitted through the body, it produces damage at junctions between tissues and air-containing organs, particularly in the chest and abdominal organs. As a consequence, lung hemorrhage and edema are likely to occur, and, if the blast effect is severe enough, air may reach the veins of the lungs and the circulatory system. This could result in death by air embolism, or suffocation by lung hemorrhage.

A main cause of physical damage resulting from a nuclear blast is the long duration of the overpressure. The length and the strength of this positive pressure phase of a nuclear blast is an important difference between nuclear and conventional explosions.

Indirect blast injuries are caused by the impact of missiles (flying debris), and physically moving the body (displacement) from its point of origin to the spot where it landed after the blast impact. The possibilities of injury from blast debris are as infinite as the number of materials, their weight, size and shape, and at what angle they strike a victim.

Displacement by a blast effect is also variable by the rate of acceleration and deceleration, and the distance a body is moved. The possibilities of injury are most likely to occur at the end of the "trip," as it would if a person were to step into an elevator shaft. The sudden drop might shake one up, but it cannot hold a candle to the sudden stop at the bottom. Displacement injury varies with the velocity of movement, the solidity of the object on which the person lands (a mattress or a brick wall), and the part of the body which absorbs the deceleration impact (the gluteus or the left ear). Of course, the size of the explosion and its distance have a direct relationship to the severity of the hazard.

Absorption of radiant energy from the intensely brilliant fireball of a nuclear explosion causes flash burns. The severity of the injury is determined by the depth and area of the burned tissue. Approximately twenty-five per cent of the deaths at Hiroshima and Nagasaki were the result of flash burns. Flame burns are those caused by the burning of combustible material resulting from overturned stoves, broken electrical wiring, or gas leaks.

The brilliance of thermal radiation is a great hazard to vision, and can cause temporary or permanent eye damage. During the 1962 nuclear tests at Johnston Island, warnings were issued hundreds of miles away in Hawaii, not to watch the fireball through binoculars because of this danger.

There are two pulses of thermal radiation from a nuclear explosion. Following quickly after the incandescent flash at the instant of ignition is the second pulse radiating eighty per cent of the thermal energy. Fast action after the burst to get out of the direct line of sight will minimize flash burn injury. This may be done by jumping behind any object which will serve as a shield, such as a tree, the corner of a building, or a doorway. If caught inside a building, it is wise to keep away from windows and dive under a table, a desk, or any nearby object. Windows pose the hazard of thermal radiation plus that of flying glass and other debris.

It has been found that clothing offers some protection if it is of light color to reflect thermal radiation. Dark cloth, or dark patterns on lighter materials, absorb heat. Many stripes and floral patterns from clothing were burned into the skin of the Hiroshima-Nagasaki victims. Thicker materials are better than thin ones, loose clothing better than tight-fitting, and more layers provide greater protection.

The introduction of nuclear weapons brought a new hazard not present in conventional explosives—nuclear radiation. Radioactivity results when atoms are split or disintegrate into subatomic particles. Alpha rays are relatively heavy particles formed from parts of the nuclei, and are positively charged. Moving at about twenty thousand miles per second for very short distances, they have little penetrating power.

Beta rays consist of streams of electrons traveling at about 170,000 miles per second. These primarily negatively charged particles also have little penetrating power. In fact, they can hardly penetrate through a piece of cardboard. Electrons are infinitesimal; form very little of the mass of an atom; and it takes about one hundred million atoms to make a line an inch long.

Gamma rays are true waves like X rays, and can penetrate through a foot of steel! They are referred to as bundles of energy. Neutrons, having no electrical charge, are slippery particles and can penetrate through much thicker steel or concrete.

Collectively, these fission fragments emit rays or particles. When a nuclear explosion occurs, billions upon billions of these fission fragments are flung out into the atmosphere. Some are in the form of specific isotopes, including: bromine, krypton, rubidium, ytterbium, strontium, columbium, molybdenum, antimony, tellurium, iodine, cesium, xenon and barium. The fission products are generally unstable and emit gamma rays and electrons during tumultuous changes and breakdowns.

Clouds of deadly poisons billow upward from an air burst following a nuclear "event." As the radioactive dust is carried up into an atomic cloud, some of the heavier particles fallout locally, and others are carried hundreds of miles, to scatter distant fallout over vast areas. Some of the radioactive materials have a short half-life, while others last for many years.

Uranium has a half-life of four-and-a-half billion years! Radium, produced by disintegrating uranium, has a half-life of 1,620 years.

Radon, a disintegration product of radium, has a half-life of less than four days. Knowing the half-life of radioactive fission products is one step toward calculating the safety and risk factors following nuclear explosions.

Iodine 131, with a half-life of eight days, nearly disintegrates in forty days, and then no longer gives off an appreciable amount of radiation. Strontium 90 has a half-life of twenty-eight years, and cesium 137 has a radioactive half-life of thirty and one-half years. The latter are bone seekers—two of the bad actors among radioisotopes abundantly present in radioactive fallout.

Physical damage from ionizing radiations is somatic and genetic. The former refers to damage to the individual during his lifetime, while the latter induces effects on his progeny. Although much has yet to be learned about genetic effects, the possibility of causing mutations in generations unborn is a disturbing thought. Added to the other devastating effects of nuclear explosions, the atomic bomb is bound to be the most unpopular product of man's ingenuity ever devised.

All of the hazards of a nuclear explosion—blast, thermal radiation, and nuclear radiation—are magnified as the yield of the explosive is increased. The twenty-kiloton bomb (equal to twenty thousand tons of TNT) dropped over Hiroshima was considered the next thing to doomsday, at the time. Now, the megaton bomb has dwarfed the "old-fashioned" nuclear explosives. A twenty-five megaton bomb (equal to twenty-five million tons of TNT) would be equivalent to a pile of one hundred billion half-pound sticks of dynamite ignited instantaneously! If stacked in one place, this dynamite would be as large as an office building a thousand feet square and reaching up into the sky another thousand feet.

The spectacular difference between this great pile of chemical explosive compared with the amount of fissionable material in a nuclear explosive is incredible. It can be explained by Einstein's equation $E = mc^2$, in which E equals Energy, m equals Mass, and c equals the Speed of light. The "speed" part of this equation is the secret to the fantastic amount of wallop in a nuclear explosion. With the speed of light computed at 186,000 miles per second, and multiplied by itself, we come up with a figure around thirty-five billion. When converting mass to energy, this is the factor explaining the tremendous energy which can be extracted from a hatful of fissionable material.

Essentially, the damaging effects of nuclear radiation are caused by ionization fragments in the body, and as a result, cells of the tissue are altered or destroyed. Ions are electrically charged particles which result when a normally neutral atom is split in such a way as to separate a negatively charged electron from the atom, leaving a positively charged fragment of an atom. Ionizing radiations disrupt the normal function of the body cells, form products which may act as poisons, destroy cells, and inhibit the necessary regeneration of cells. The manifestations of cellular damage or action of poison is known as radiation sickness.

The initial nuclear radiation, occurring during the first minute after an explosion, consists of gamma rays and neutrons. The dosages are expressed in terms of rems; biologically equivalent to one roentgen of X-ray or gamma radiation. Although a dose of one hundred rems throughout the body would not affect an individual observably, his chances of survival after four hundred and fifty rems would be fifty per cent. With a dose of one thousand rems over his entire body, he would not survive more than four or five weeks.

Initial radiations from high-yield explosives allow a second or two of time before arrival, if one should be far enough away to survive the blast and intense thermal radiation. If not, death would come three ways at once. Although protective clothing will help against thermal radiation, it will provide little shielding against initial nuclear radiation.

Residual nuclear radiation is a somewhat different phenomenon than initial nuclear radiation. The area of residual nuclear fallout covers a much larger area than that affected by blast, heat, and initial radiation. The insidious residual effects result from the great distances at which people can become infected, depending on the wind, and other atmospheric conditions. Also, the unsuspecting victims experience no immediate effects to cause them concern. An explosion in the megaton range might contaminate areas several hundred miles away from the burst, with a two-day lapse before dangerous radiation fallout begins to arrive.

Early fallout produces two effects. One is caused by the contact of radioactive material on the skin, producing beta burns. The other effect is caused by exposure to gamma rays from fallout residue. Beta burns can be avoided by immediately washing the skin with soap and water. Gamma rays, however, are not so easily dissuaded from penetrating and damaging tissue.

Thick layers of earth or concrete are necessary to lessen the penetration of gamma rays incident to residual nuclear radiation. An eight-inch wall of concrete, or one foot of earth, will reduce gamma penetration ten times. Doubling the thickness will reduce penetration by another factor of ten, which would make a sixteen-inch concrete wall one hundred times as effective as no protection at all. However, unlike thermal radiation, the protection must cover completely since gamma radiations scatter throughout the atmosphere.

It requires about a week's time before the radiation level drops to one-tenth of the initial level. Because of the long duration of gamma radiation contamination, and the unlikely availability of a handy, enclosed structure of sixteen-inch concrete, distance is the best salvation if there is a means of providing mobility. A naval or military force which has mobility, not mere movability, has the option of running out of an area contaminated by nuclear radiation fallout. The words of Horace, whose wisdom was not as suspect as his bravery, apply in this situation: "A good run is better than a poor stand."

In any fixed complex on land, such as storage areas, air fields, industrial complexes, or military bases, the safety factor of mobility is eliminated. Installations attached to any piece of land can hardly avoid being permanently zeroed-in by an adversary with a nuclear weapon, and a means of delivery. Deployed naval forces therefore have an immediate survival advantage over other elements of the armed forces. Aircraft which must operate from a fixed base do not have the same advantage as carrier-based planes; only while they are airborne do they have sporadic periods of mobility. For fueling, rearming, servicing, overhaul, and rest for the aircrews, land-based aircraft are tied to a series of air bases on stationary pieces of real estate.

The basic mobility of deployed naval forces affords a means of providing distance from a likely target area. It is said that distance lends enchantment, and the greater distance, the better, from a kiloton or megaton nuclear explosion.

If all naval forces were embarked in modern, nuclear, sealed-from-the-atmosphere ships, capable of quickly steaming away from a potentially contaminated area, there would be less concern about exposure to radiation. However, Navy men and Marines stationed on terra firma at naval shore installations, cannot seal themselves from the atmosphere, ring up "four bells and a jingle," and disappear over the horizon. They must be prepared to take necessary precautions to avoid ingesting food and water contaminated by radioactive fallout.

Storing emergency supplies of food and water in air-tight containers is a recommended procedure. Although radioactive dust may settle on the exterior of the containers, they may be washed before opening, and the contents consumed without risking significant contamination. Water exposed to the air cannot be consumed without specific processing for radioactivity. Chlorination or boiling kills bacteria, but is not effective in eliminating radioactivity.

Inhaling air filled with radioactive dust is another means of internal radiation exposure. Although inhalation imparts relatively small amounts of radioactive material into the body, compared with ingestion, breathing through a protective respiratory filter is recommended until monitoring equipment indicates the air to be safe.

The Naval Radiological Defense Laboratory, under the management control of the Bureau of Ships, was the first organization to acquire experience in handling radioactivity in ships contaminated by fallout from nuclear explosions. Nuclear tests create situations involving a high level of radioactivity. At such times it might become necessary to exceed safe exposure limits. However, individual and group exposures are kept to a minimum by various protective measures, such as: controlling the duration of time in radioactively "hot" areas; wearing protective clothing and respirators; using remote handling tools or radio-controlled equipment such as drone aircraft and boats in Operation Crossroads; and limiting personnel who enter a contaminated area to the radiological control (RadCon) teams until it is declared safe.

Many of the techniques used in monitoring and decontaminating non-target ships returning from Operation Crossroads at Bikini were sound procedure in a pioneer field, and are still in use. Furthermore, many of the people from NRDL were able to apply their valuable experience in numerous subsequent nuclear tests in Nevada and in the Pacific.

The huge fifteen-megaton thermonuclear explosion set off at Bikini Atoll in March, 1954, provided information on the extent of the area affected by a giant nuclear blast. The pattern of contamination extended downwind three hundred and thirty miles in an irregular pattern, spreading over sixty miles at its widest point. It reached upwind for twenty miles. The entire area of severe contamination covered over seven thousand square miles.

In escaping from fallout, wind velocity and direction must be considered, as well as the direction of the blast, in relationship to the ship and the wind. If a commanding officer is lucky, the nuclear explosion will be downwind from his ship, and simplify his problem. If not, he will have to decide on an "end run" to the left or the right.

[161]

One decision need hardly be made—if the ship has any kind of speed, this would be a good time to use it!

If it should be necessary to steam through radioactive fallout, the advantage of a completely sealed-in ship with a washdown system, and a nuclear power plant, is self-evident. Other ships must draw in oxygen for oil-burning, or diesel, power plants. As air is drawn in, the ambient radioactivity comes in with it. However, conventionally powered ships can keep out fission particles fairly well by closing ports and hatches, and shutting off the air ventilation system temporarily, until the ship has passed through the probable area of dangerous fallout.

Mobility and the availability of plenty of water for radioactive washdown give Navy ships two distinct advantages in nuclear warfare. The atomic washdown system, a series of spray nozzles around topside areas of a ship, may be turned on to wash off radioactive fallout which might settle on the exposed parts of the ship. Following the washdown, monitoring teams with Geiger counters and other detection instruments determine when the ship is again radioactively safe. Decontamination lockers in our combatant ships provide means of "sanitizing" personnel, clothing, and equipment used in cleaning up and monitoring all areas and spaces following a nuclear attack, or other source of radiation exposure.

Naval tacticians required answers to basic questions. How far must a ship be from a nuclear explosion to avoid being sunk? How great must the distance vary with the magnitude? How far apart must ships be spaced in a task group formation to prevent losing more than one ship, if any, per explosion? What avoiding action can be taken? Should personnel at topside stations remain, or should they rush below decks for protection? Should concentrations of ships in harbors be limited? What new naval tactics are required? How should ship design be modified? In short, what must be done toward adapting our Navy for the nuclear age, now and in the future?

The nuclear test explosions at Bikini, in 1946, marked a point of departure in naval thinking. The impact of the new art of nuclear warfare extended to ship design, naval tactics, scientific research, training of personnel, and developing new doctrine for nuclear weapons and radiological defense. When confronted with an atomic attack, the goal is to keep our ships steaming, propellers turning, planes flying, and missiles launching.

The awesome spectacle of dazzling light, and peach-colored clouds from a nuclear explosion is somewhat deceptive—like a velvet glove covering an iron fist. The very foundations of strategy and tactics were shaken by this new force in warfare. Survival under the nuclear mushroom cloud is a matter of urgent business, and the first requirement toward retaliation against a nuclear attack.

FOURTEEN

A Spectrum of Weapons

WARS in the past have inspired poets and philosophers with words of inspiration and wisdom. Opposing armies, mounted and on foot, arrayed themselves against each other, and waited for the trumpets' blast. They then charged with banners bravely fluttering, armor gleaming, and brave men dying under the clash of swords. But the bards will be hard-pressed to capture any pageantry and glory of future wars. They would be fought with long-range weapons, fired by an unseen enemy, far away from the target.

The age of chivalrous warfare is long past; the war hero is vanishing. When David and Goliath faced each other, with armies watching, the score was one dead and one live hero. By contrast, a nuclear weapon can wipe out a city. Heroes of any kind would be hard to find after mass annihilation resulting from one giant, incandescent flash of light.

The modern warrior will be surrounded, not by his enemy in hand-to-hand combat, but by an array of panels loaded with electronic gear. His eye will be alert to changes in instrument readings, and colored lights flashing on and off. His adversary may not be a man, or a group of men, but a target complex. Advances in weaponry have made warfare more and more impersonal; from swords and spears, to guns and grenades, to rockets and missiles.

World conflicts have spread far beyond defined battle areas, and in the process have destroyed cities and industrial complexes, taking an ever-increasing toll among civilians. Of the 9,800,000 killed in

World War I, five per cent were civilians. World War II took 52,000,000 lives, forty-eight per cent of whom were civilians. The war in Korea killed 9,200,000, and over eighty per cent of them were civilians.

The first nuclear test explosion in the desert at Alamagordo, New Mexico, set off more than a nuclear chain reaction—it brought about a reaction in new concepts of waging war. When General MacArthur first heard of the proposed A-bomb drop over Japan, in August, 1945, his immediate reaction was that it would "change all our ideas of warfare." (Earlier, at the Potsdam Conference in July, when President Truman told Stalin about the new, powerful weapon planned for use against Japan, it made little visible impression on him. As it later developed, Stalin knew about it long before the meeting.)

Progress in nuclear explosives advanced so fast that by March, 1954 the super bomb tested at Bikini had dwarfed the nuclear bombs used in World War II. This thermonuclear explosion (fifteen megatons), erupted with a force seven hundred and fifty times more powerful than the bomb dropped over Hiroshima. The "old-fashioned" bombs (twenty kilotons), were about the right yield for use as a detonator for the thermonuclear, fission-fusion-fission device. The three-in-one nuclear explosion first involves splitting the heaviest atoms, U-235 or P-239; creating the tremendous heat which sets off the fusion reaction of our lightest atoms, hydrogen. High-energy neutrons released by the fusion reaction triggers the "fast fission" reaction of the common, inexpensive type of uranium, U-238. The common uranium jacket placed around the hydrogen explosive gives a relatively inexpensive "bonus bang." However, since it explodes in the same instant, and at the same spot, as the thermonuclear device, its usefulness is limited.

We have the ability to make nuclear weapons as powerful as we want them to be. The question arises whether the explosives are ten or a thousand times more powerful than required to do a specific job. The principle of "overkill" has consequently come up for review.

It might be compared with blasting an ant with a shotgun, when the cork at the end of a popgun would render the ant just as dead.

Progress in developing nuclear weapons has not been confined to making them larger. An equally challenging task was the job of making them smaller so they could be adapted to a wider spectrum of weapons. Small weapons described as "sub-kil" (having an explosive yield less than one thousand tons of TNT) are possible. However, the question arises whether the complications of handling sub-kil, special weapons, and the tactics required for their delivery, would warrant their development.

Another question is, why use nuclear weapons at all? If their use, however small, were permitted, would it not escalate a war into a massive nuclear exchange? If there is to be a limit on explosive yield, who is to set the limit? Who will make sure that the participants will adhere to an international agreement? Furthermore, if military forces are going to use small nuclear explosives, why not use conventional weapons?

The spectrum of nuclear and conventional weapons includes the various means of delivery, as well as differing magnitudes of yield. If it were desirable, most of our weapons could be adapted for a nuclear warhead. Since it is not desirable, it is imperative that we maintain a good array of conventional weapons to supplement our nuclear capability.

Classifying our various weapons could be done by different kinds of naval forces, such as ASW, amphibious, mine, air strike, or undersea. However, the missile age has created its own categories by its great diversity in the types of launches and proposed targets. As a result, we have: air-to-air missiles (AAM); air-to-surface (ASM); air-to-underwater (AUM); surface-to-air (SAM); surface-to-surface (SSM); surface-to-underwater (SUM); underwater-to-underwater (UUM); and underwater-to-surface missiles (USM).

Air-to-air missiles are those fired from aircraft to knock out air targets. Two of the Navy's mainstays in the AAM type are Sparrow

III and Sidewinder. Weighing about three hundred and eighty pounds, the twelve-foot Sparrow III is an all-weather, radar-homing missile, with a solid propellant. A high performance missile, it can blast a fast-moving jet from any angle with an operational ceiling over fifty thousand feet.

The Sidewinder missile, a reliable, inexpensive weapon about nine feet in length and weighing one hundred and fifty-five pounds, is a heatseeker. Traveling at supersonic speed, with a solid propellant, it also has a ceiling over fifty thousand feet. When first used in the Korean War, it streaked after Russian-built jets, climbed up their hot tail pipes, and "surprised" the Communist pilots. Simple in construction, with few moving parts, Sidewinder is also used by the Marine Corps and Air Force. This jewel of a weapon was developed at the Naval Ordnance Test Station (NOTS), China Lake, California, and was the brainchild of Dr. William B. McLean, the Technical Director.

There are many other air-to-air weapons such as rockets, cannon, and machine guns. However, unlike a missile, these projectiles have no guidance while in flight. Sometimes called "a rocket with brains," a missile can make corrective course changes in pursuing a target after firing.

Air-to-surface (ASM) missiles are fired from aircraft against targets on land or afloat. Bullpup, as originally conceived, was a two hundred and fifty-pound bomb with a rocket motor and a guidance system. Now a family of weapons, Bullpup is widely used by the Air Force and NATO countries. It can be fitted with a conventional or nuclear warhead, and guided accurately without the necessity for the aircraft to follow it into close proximity of the surface target after launch.

Shrike is another Navy air-to-surface missile developed as an anti-radar weapon. Adapting some of the components of other missile systems already used in the fleet, the Navy has taken some money-saving shortcuts to provide our aircraft with increased high-speed, guided "clobber capability."

In the rocket category, Zuni is a greatly improved, five-inch-diameter, high-velocity, air-to--ground, or air-to-air, rocket. By using folding fins, aircraft can carry four times as many Zuni rounds, fired singly or in a ripple salvo. The Zuni also can be fitted with a variety of interchangeable warheads to "accommodate" different kinds of targets.

A whole family of air-to-surface weapons of the "eye" series has been developed at NOTS, China Lake. They are unguided, free-fall weapons designed for conventional warfare, and named for their means of guidance by the old-fashioned, human eye. Walleye is a homing glide weapon which can accurately hit visual targets. Snakeye is a retardation device, attached to 250- or 500-pound bombs to slow them down after being dropped at a low level, while the aircraft streaks ahead. This permits the plane to clear the area before the effects of the weapon can damage it.

Rockeye is fired from a rocket, and dispenses a large cluster of explosives to impact over a poorly defined target, or to compensate for drop errors intrinsic to high-speed aircraft with unguided weapons. Rockeye II, with a bigger wallop, is useful as an anti-tank or anti-personnel cluster weapon.

Sadeye has many uses; it is known as a universal weapon dispenser. Scattering a large payload over a wide target area, Sadeye can meet many tactical requirements, and can be delivered by various aircraft bombing techniques: loft, toss, glide, dive, or level bombing runs. Fireye, using jellied gasoline or jet fuel, drops a long-lasting flame on ground targets. The "eye" series is expanding into a large number of tactical weapons designed to give any enemy a real "eye full."

Air-to-underwater (AUM) missiles include a variety of aerial torpedoes and depth charges designed primarily to destroy ships and submarines. Betty, the atomic depth charge, is an operational nuclear weapon with a potent "knock-out" punch which can be air-dropped by ASW aircraft. The Mark 46 torpedo, having a guidance system, is designed particularly to destroy fast, deep-diving nuclear submarines.

However, detecting submarines continues to be the difficult problem rather than destroying them once located.

Air-dropped torpedoes can be used for special targets such as the aerial torpedo dropped by a Navy plane during the Korean War to blast the Wachon Reservoir. Air-dropped mines are equipped with "brains." These weapons are tricky and deadly, and can be adapted for conventional or nuclear explosives.

Surface-to-air (SAM) missiles are replacing antiaircraft guns, particularly for long-range interception of supersonic enemy aircraft. The Navy's longest-range SAM is thirty-foot-long Talos, powered by a solid fuel booster and a ramjet engine. With a range of over fifty miles, Talos is a "beam rider," having a homing guidance system. Equipped with either a conventional or nuclear warhead, it can be used effectively against air or surface targets.

A smaller SAM, Terrier, is twenty-seven feet long, with booster attached, and has a range of more than fifteen miles. In seconds, a Terrier missile can be selected from the ship's magazine, loaded on the launcher, whipped into the right direction and elevation, and launched. Guided to the target by a radar beam, Terrier can blast high-flying jet aircraft before they arrive over a task group. They can be adapted for nuclear warheads, used against air targets, and are installed in combatant ships or used ashore by Marines.

Tartar is the smallest member of the "Terrible T" family of guided SAM-types in the Navy. It has a solid fuel, dual-thrust rocket motor which gives it a range of over ten miles. Tartar is the main armament of guided missile destroyers for use in air defense.

A surface-to-surface (SSM) missile, Regulus I, can be launched from surface ships as well as submarines. It has a range of five hundred miles, and must be fired from the surface because it uses an air-breathing engine. A reliable guided missile, it can pack a wallop with its nuclear warhead. Designed primarily for submarine employment, Regulus has had to take a back seat to the more spectacular Polaris.

The mainstay of surface-to-underwater (SUM) missiles is ASROC (AntiSubmarine ROCket), a shipboard ASW weapons system with four integrated major parts: sonar underwater detection gear; fire control system; a launcher which holds eight missiles; and the missiles themselves. ASROC is fifteen feet in length, and weighs a thousand pounds. It consists of a solid-fuel rocket motor, an air frame, and the payload in the form of a nuclear depth charge, or an acoustic homing torpedo.

By sending out short sounds, the ship's sonar can calculate a submarine's position and movement, compute its future position, and, through its fire-control system, give orders to the missile. When launched, ASROC starts out as an air missile. Seconds after firing, the rocket booster falls away, and the torpedo continues through the air. Before plunging into the water, the air frame falls away, and a small parachute assists in an orderly entry into the water. The homing torpedo then commences a search for the target, locks on, and destroys it with a conventional explosive. A stand-off and reach-out weapon of this type is required against fast, non-surfacing nuclear submarines which are hard to catch up with in a sea chase.

Underwater-to-underwater (UUM) missiles are submarine-fired weapons designed to explode under the water. The SUBROC weapon, although an UUM, does not remain under the water, but takes off through the surface and re-enters the water where it explodes near enough to a target submarine to effect a "kill." Torpedoes, also in the UUM class, remain underwater from the time of launch to the point of impact. They may be directed toward a submarine or a surface ship, but in either case, the impact is below the surface.

In the underwater-to-surface (USM) missile, the Navy has the blue-and-gold "ribbon winner"—Polaris. On station along advanced defense positions, Polaris, among the Navy's spectrum of weapons, is our most reliable "stopper" against any nation contemplating a nuclear exchange.

The difference between a tactical and a strategic weapon is often confused merely with long-range delivery, and the size of the explosive impact on the target. Under this superficial definition, more and more weapons would automatically become classed as strategic because of the trend toward long-range delivery and high-yield explosives.

When a weapon such as Polaris affects national and international policies, it clearly comes within the broader connotation of the word "strategic." Coincidentally, this weapon is launched a long way from its target, and explodes with tremendous force. However, it is the international deterrent pressure put upon a potential aggressor which makes Polaris a powerful strategic weapon.

Firing from the air, the surface, or under the sea, the Navy has a most potent array of nuclear and conventional weapons. Any enemy of the United States would be foolhardy to challenge this tremendous fire power, when added to that of our Army and Air Force. To safeguard the free nations of the world, Polaris, the *aurora borealis* in our spectrum of weapons, stands ready and in position today.

FIFTEEN

Polaris—A Weapon of Peace

ANYONE who has taken an ocean voyage across the vast Atlantic or Pacific must be greatly impressed by the seemingly endless stretches of water. As your ship steadily knifes through waves and whitecaps, the foamy water rushes by in myriad patterns, and disappears astern. Miles pass into hundreds and then thousands of miles of undulating water. To the north and south, the sea stretches for more thousands of miles of tossing, heaving ocean. Down, down into the water for hundreds of fathoms, the gradually darkening depths provide the world's greatest hiding place. This is the domain of the Polaris submarine.

From the launching tube, the Polaris Fleet Ballistic Missile is fired from the ocean depths, leaps to the surface, and ignites with a terrifying roar as it climbs into the sky toward its target. Thrust from within the domain of Neptunus Rex, Polaris can strike any area on earth with thermonuclear terror. The traditional threat of the submarine is no longer confined to the sea lanes. A munitions plant, an air base, or a city can be wiped out by our new strategic submarine threat—the Polaris missile.

The Polaris missile system, with its electronic, automated controls, nuclear-propelled launching platform, and accurate thermonuclear warheads, is fantastic in its technology. However, without the very competent men who operate the system, it could not function.

Commander George Steele, skipper of the first Polaris submarine in the Pacific Fleet, USS *Daniel Boone,* compared his command to a battleship: "Submarines have really grown up over the past ten years. Automation, miniaturization and computers have changed the submariner's life from relative simplicity and personal decision to a life surrounded by the most complex equipment ever installed in a single ship. The principal wonder is that human beings are able to adapt themselves to such a change in such a short time."

With their Blue and Gold crew rotations, each Polaris submarine requires about two hundred and seventy submariners for the two carefully selected, highly trained crews. While one crew of approximately one hundred and thirty-five officers and men is out on patrol, the other returns to home port and families at New London, Connecticut; Charleston, South Carolina; and Pearl Harbor, Hawaii. The submarine schools and Fleet Ballistic Missile (FBM) training facilities are also located there, and after a period of leave, the crews commence refresher training on a five-day weekly schedule. During this time they prepare for the next patrol at sea, practice on the complex FBM trainer, and the new crew members work together with the experienced men just as they would on patrol.

Not all of those in the Polaris program go to sea in FBM submarines. Some are assigned to support facilities, including missile testing and assembly, training, shipbuilding, specially equipped ships for navigational tests, experimental test firing, and tending and supplying FBM submarines. Together, the submarine, missiles, and men constitute the Polaris FBM system. Support facilities, well-trained personnel, and control and communications facets are highly important in the overall program. All of this came into existence through magnificent cooperation between the Navy, science, and industry.

In 1955, the Polaris program was tied to the U.S. Army's Jupiter missile development. It did not take long to realize the disadvantages of this type of missile for shipboard use. A missile forty-five feet in length and weighing seventy-five tons was out of the question. The missile, the nuclear warhead, and the guidance system all had the same kind of problems—too big and too heavy.

The liquid propellant was dangerous and had a short stowage

life. While a solid propellant would remove these obstacles, nothing satisfactory had yet been developed. This was only one of many parts still missing in the Polaris project. The fire control and navigation system, communications, and the configuration of the missile itself had to be perfected. Even the mobile missile launching platform—the submarine itself—had yet to be designed and built.

Recognizing the problems, and solving them within the short time frame, set technological goals which constituted a crash program barely within the realm of possibility. The entire Polaris program then was moved ahead from 1963 to 1960, and placed under a newly created Special Projects Office, headed by Vice Adm. William F. Raborn (then a rear admiral). Capt. Levering Smith was the technical director and coordinator.

A new management technique was applied to the entire Polaris program called PERT (Program Evaluation and Review Technique). It employs a computerized analysis of problems and highlights the trouble areas in order to meet the critical time schedule. By introducing PERT into the management, the great number of complex parts and components of the Polaris program were time-phased into the final weapons system—on schedule. PERT was widely adopted by industry and other programs because of its great success in Admiral Raborn's Special Projects Office.

Altogether, some thirty thousand contractors and government agencies' personnel worked on the FBM system. Aerojet General Corporation came through with a high-energy, solid-propellant rocket motor, bringing it down to an acceptable size. Dr. C. S. Draper of the Massachusetts Institute of Technology provided an inertial guidance system well below the weight of any other system. The Atomic Energy Commission developed a nuclear warhead with high explosive yield and great reduction in weight. The well-known nuclear physicist, Dr. Edward Teller, and his associates improved on the explosive yield with a thermonuclear warhead. Lockheed, the prime contractor for the Polaris missile, submitted proposals for a number of two-stage missile configurations with finless, jetevator controls for accuracy in flight trajectories.

The Electric Boat Division of General Dynamics built the first Polaris FBM submarine. Before the missile was developed, the USS *George Washington* was under construction (originally it had been laid down as USS *Scorpion*). By cutting her into two parts and adding a 130-foot section in the middle, she was converted to the first FBM submarine, and commissioned on December 30, 1959. She launched the first Polaris missile on July 20, 1960, and deployed with sixteen ready missiles on November 15.

The first five Polaris submarines were of the *George Washington* class—380 feet in length and displacing 5,900 tons. The next five, commencing with USS *Ethan Allen,* were 410 feet long and displaced 6,900 tons. Still growing in size, the *Lafayette* class measured 425 feet from stem to stern and weighed 7,320 tons.

While the submarines have become bigger and better, the missiles have also improved. The A-1 Polaris missile, initially carried by the *George Washington* class submarines, had a range of 1,380 statute miles. The A-2 missiles, first carried in ships of the *Ethan Allen* class, extended the range to 1,725 miles. The bullet-shaped A-3 Polaris departed from the bottle shape of her predecessors. With a range of 2,880 miles, it can reach any land target in the world from a submerged launching position.

All three types are two-stage ballistic missiles propelled by solid fuel rocket motors. Most FBM submarines eventually will be equipped to launch the A-3 Polaris missiles. The motor cases of the first and second stage of the missiles are made of glass fiber, making the A-3 missiles much lighter than those with steel casings, while retaining the required strength.

The first stage is controlled in flight by rotating nozzles, while the second stage employs a fluid injection system. The 2,500-nautical mile range (2,880 statute miles) of the A-3 reaches distant targets, and also provides the submarine with a larger patrol area. With the assumption that a target is 1,000 miles inland, the A-1 Polaris missile would permit the submarine 690,800 square miles of sea room for concealment. Under the same conditions, the A-3 missile enlarges the patrol area to 8,242,500 square miles; a spectacular increase in safety and survivability.

Now under development is a new generation of missiles named Poseidon, designed for FBM submarines. Costing two billion dollars to develop and produce, Poseidon will double the thermonuclear payload of the A-3 Polaris while at the same time increasing the accuracy. This will permit a broadened range of use to include hardened (underground and heavily protected) military targets such as missile bases. Our Polaris submarines, still looking to the future, may carry a mixed load of Polaris and Poseidon missiles during patrols in the 1970's.

During a patrol, each submarine is assigned an area within range of the assigned targets. If an FBM submarine encounters a strange ship, it takes evasive action and, if necessary, it can fire torpedoes in self-defense. As it moves around within this area, Polaris submarines stress constant readiness.

A key piece of equipment in a Polaris submarine is the Ship's Inertial Navigation System (SINS), a complex system of gyroscopes and accelerometers which keeps track of the ship's movement in any direction. The missiles receive continuous information from SINS telling exactly where the submarine is located, true north, the target location, and the trajectory to be flown. Constant changes from the moving submarine are imparted to the Polaris missile until the instant of launching.

Past experience has shown a remarkable record of keeping missiles in an up-and-ready status. On the average, fifteen of the missiles have been ready to launch ninety-nine per cent of the time, and all sixteen have been ready over ninety-five per cent of the time. The fire control system is capable of preparing the sixteen missiles for launching at a rate of less than one per minute. This is a refreshing contrast from the long countdown, and hours or even days, of delay associated with many of the liquid-propelled missiles launched from coastal bases in Florida and California.

The principal FBM test site is at Cape Kennedy, Florida, where the Polaris complex includes launching pads, missile assembly, and check-out buildings with supply and maintenance facilities. Other important tests were conducted aboard ships and along the California coast, particularly during early development.

USS *Compass Island* (EAG-153), the FBM navigation development and test ship, began her operations in January of 1957. She cruised more than one hundred thousand nautical miles testing and perfecting the accuracy of SINS. In November of that year, the compressed air launching subsystem was checked out during "Operation Peashooter" at the San Francisco Naval Shipyard. The first test flight of a fleet ballistic missile took place at Point Mugu, California, in January, 1958, and by March the initial submerged launching, named "Popup," was fired off San Clemente Island.

Step by step, the Polaris FBM was developed and tested. The first seaborne solid propellant ballistic missile was launched from the experimental test ship USS *Observation Island* (EAG-154) off the Florida coast in August, 1959. The following March she successfully launched a missile using the fully integrated FBM system, including submarine-type navigation, fire control, and launching equipment, with an inertially guided missile. There remained one final test—launching from a submarine.

On July 20, 1960, USS *George Washington* successfully fired off the Florida coast two Polaris missiles while submerged. This was a great day for the Navy, and for Vice Adm. William F. Raborn, who had been in charge of developing the Polaris FBM system since December, 1955. Each part of the Polaris program was under simultaneous development, and the revolutionary FBM weapon leaped far ahead of anything yet conceived.

To support the Polaris program, the Naval Weapons Annex was

established at the Ammunition Depot at Charleston, South Carolina, as a missile assembly point for Polaris submarines of the Atlantic Fleet. The same function is performed at the Naval Ammunition Depot in Bangor, Washington for FBM submarines operating in the Pacific. All subsystems and sections of Polaris missiles are received from manufacturers at these two places for assembly, check-out, and storage, until they are loaded into Polaris submarines or support ships.

The specially Polaris-equipped submarine tenders will serve the FBM submarines at Holy Loch, Scotland; Rota, Spain; Charleston, South Carolina; Melville, Rhode Island; and Apra Harbor, Guam. Four of the submarine tenders in the Polaris support program are USS *Proteus* (AS-19), USS *Hunley* (AS-31), USS *Holland* (AS-32), and USS *Simon Lake* (AS-33). A total of six tenders are planned to supply and service the submarines for everything short of major repairs. By stationing them in forward locations, transit time to patrol areas is saved with each crew change.

In order to keep the FBM submarine tenders supplied with everything from boneless beef to ball bearings, six re-supply ships will become part of the program. The first three in service were USS *Alcor* (AK-259), USS *Betelgeuse* (AK-260), and USS *Norwalk* (TAK-279).

In the vital area of communications support and control, Polaris submarines maintain a constant vigil on the Navy's worldwide radio communication system. Their twenty-four-hour watch continues every day of the year from a position well on the way to their targets. The authority to launch missiles must come from the Commander in Chief in the White House. Needless to say, the communication link is of paramount importance.

The target selection for Polaris missiles is under the control of the Joint Chiefs of Staff, as are other strategic weapons of our retaliatory force. Both the assignment of targets, and the initiative to launch the missiles, rests with higher authority than the individual FBM sub-

[178]

marine skippers. Their job is to be constantly "on the line" when, and if, it becomes necessary to launch their lethal "birds" in national defense. To render unauthorized firings impossible, a series of interlocks and alarms is installed in the launch system.

Should it be necessary—and authorized—only the commanding officer of an FBM submarine could order the launching of a missile. When USS *Ethan Allen* fired the first Polaris with a nuclear warhead in a test launch, this command-control procedure was used.

Comdr. Russell McWey stood by the weapon control center watching the green, red, and amber lights. He could not launch the live A-1 Polaris missile until the skipper of the Blue crew, Capt. Paul L. Lacy, pushed the green light button. As Commander McWey emphasized: "The skipper definitely has control."

Captain Lacy confirmed this control procedure but added: "McWey actually fired the missile. There were no incidents in connection with this launching. Everyone involved was so well-trained in his job that it was routine. Of course, there was a certain amount of excitement among the crew; knowing this missile carried a nuclear warhead."

One would think that firing a fifteen-ton missile would cause a violent reaction throughout the submarine. However, this is not the case. When the missile is forced out of the tube, it pops out very quickly. Back in the missile compartment there is a rushing sound of changing pressures, but in the control compartment where the skipper is stationed there is nothing more than a "thump"—and the "bird" is gone. The submarine has proven a very stable launching platform; its liquid environment is useful as a shock-absorber, and for counterflooding missile tubes to maintain the same weight with or without the missile.

By the end of 1964, thirty-two Polaris submarines had been launched, and twenty-eight of the thirty-two were commissioned. By 1967, it is planned that the total goal of forty-one FBM submarines will be operational in the Atlantic and Pacific Fleets. The purpose of this potent force of Polaris submarines is to deter any aggressor nation from a rash violation of the peace which might ignite a nuclear war.

Rear Adm. I. J. Galantin, who succeeded Vice Admiral Raborn as Director of Special Projects, has pointed out some of the special qualities of the Polaris system:

"The unique ingredient which our Polaris submarines bring to our national strategic retaliatory systems is that of concealment. This, added to the Navy's inherent mobility, creates a system of such invulnerability that it is of greatest effect as a deterrent. Because it need not be invoked at an early moment for fear of destruction, it gives time for mature deliberation before its use. Furthermore, it need not be unleashed in one furious blast. It can be applied selectively in measured, precise fashion.

"In addition, it is clearly apparent that any attacks upon our Polaris submarines hidden at sea would not result in collateral damage upon our own territory. For these reasons, I believe the Polaris system in this era of weapons of mass destruction in a world groping toward an effectively controlled disarmament, is a most stabilizing influence."

The Polaris submarine concept takes our allies off the spot by providing launching bases away from their home territory. Also, fewer strategic targets, such as land-based missile launching sites, is a great defensive advantage. This advantage applies for the United States, as well as for Great Britain, whose land area is much smaller, and may have been one of the deciding factors in Great Britain's participation in the Polaris program. Although she uses United States-built Polaris missiles, she is building her own FBM submarines for the Royal Navy.

The great destructive power of Polaris missiles is a most impressive force for any nation to contemplate if it is considering a nuclear assault against the free world. In a speech at the Electric Boat shipyard at Groton, Connecticut, in June, 1964, President Lyndon B.

Johnson stated: "One of these subs armed with sixteen Polaris missiles has an explosive punch greater than all the destructive power unleashed by all the guns, cannons, planes, and ships on both sides during all of World War II."

If potential aggressor nations are to be deterred by the Polaris force, they must realize, with certainty, the horrible retaliation they will bring upon themselves.

When Secretary of the Navy Paul H. Nitze spoke at the commissioning of the Polaris Missile Facility at Bangor, Washington in September, 1964, he said: "With respect to penetration capability, the actual damage which Polaris can do by itself—now—with the forces which are currently deployed, is staggering. If a nuclear attack were launched by an enemy against American cities, and we had only our present Polaris on-station force with which to retaliate, personnel fatalities in the target areas in the aggressor nation would be between thirty and forty million.

"Our Polaris forces alone are capable of inflicting damage of such major proportions to enemy war-making capability that initiating of nuclear war by any enemy would be an irrational act. Our Polaris submarines are a strong backbone of striking power, which even if they stood alone, would constitute a powerful deterrent."

No nation in history has spent so much money and effort on something it hopes never to use. Today, the world is without adequate international control of nuclear weapons, while the number and power of nuclear nations are increasing. However, the United States has a great stabilizing force against the bandits among national powers. On station under the sea, Polaris submarines serve as international policemen. They carry "a big stick"—Polaris, a weapon of peace.

SIXTEEN

The World Ponders the Atom

WE KNEW from the hardware history of Polaris that it had proven itself. It was a bold advance in missilery, using the depth and breadth of the oceans as a concealed "launching pad." The question remaining unanswered was: "Will it deter an aggressor nation from starting a war?"

One of the requirements of a powerful deterrent is full knowledge on the part of an aggressor concerning the devastating retaliation he will suffer should he violate the peace. The severity of the consequences should be a deterrent to aggression; the punishment should be so harsh that the violator cannot afford it. No nation could withstand being "clobbered" by sixteen, thirty-two, or two hundred Polaris missiles.

Inadvertently, former Soviet Premier Khrushchev played an important part in testing the deterrent power of the Polaris missile system. His proving ground was not on a missile range, but on the international cold war scene. He reacted to Polaris as though he realized that he could not afford retaliation by thermonuclear-tipped Polaris missiles.

In a speech at Port Said in May, 1964, the Soviet Premier urged the Egyptians and the Arab nations to join Russia in barring Polaris submarines from the Mediterranean. In his first bid to encourage Arab nations to take an open stand against the United States, Khrushchev tried to frighten the leaders by saying: "The Atlantic strategists are trying to turn the Mediterranean basin into a big rocket drome, ignoring the vital interests of the peoples of those countries." What Khrushchev failed to add was his concern that the missile targets might have an address in the U.S.S.R.

During disarmament talks at Geneva in the spring of 1964, the Soviet Delegate Semyon K. Tsarapkin declared, "The Polaris is antihumanistic and antidisarmament, and must be done away with." Just why the Fleet Ballistic Missile Polaris is more dangerous to world peace than land-based missiles was not made clear by Tsarapkin. It is part of the Communist method to attempt to "do away" with something held in the U.S. arsenal, while retaining whatever the U.S.S.R. happens to have ready. It is also clear that the Polaris system is one to which the Soviet Union presently has no answer. Until a miracle of world disarmament comes about, Polaris remains a deterrent to all-out war.

With worldwide deployment of Polaris submarines on patrol, these "watchdogs" of our national security are a sure and reliable force. They are practically invulnerable from attack, and if one were ever knocked out, the retaliation (upon Presidential order) from the others on patrol would be awesome indeed.

Since the United States does not intend to be the first to fire a nuclear missile in any international exchange, great importance must be given to the survival factor. To retaliate, a weapons system must survive an initial attack. In reliability—and survivability—the Polaris submarine must be acknowledged as having no equal.

Although our Polaris submarine force is committed to fulfill defense obligations to NATO countries, it is a national force of the United States. The British have a nuclear air and missile force, while the French are developing a small, nuclear *force de frappe*. In order to give all our NATO partners an opportunity to participate in a nuclear force, and share in the responsibility, manning, and cost, a MultiLateral Force (MLF) has been proposed.

In essence, the MLF was conceived as a strategic missile force consisting of about twenty-five ships with merchant-type hulls, each armed with eight Polaris missiles. Such a force would place two hundred medium-range ballistic missiles "on the line" to augment national deterrent forces, and would be dispersed over three to four million square miles of the Atlantic and Mediterranean. The ships would be manned by a mixed ship's company of six, or more, of the NATO nations. None of the countries represented would have more than forty percent of the total overall personnel, and no single ship would have more than forty percent of one nationality.

As proposed, the MLF would give NATO nations an opportunity to have a greater voice in employment of nuclear weapons, and it would permit participation on the part of all NATO countries in nuclear defense strategy. This would further unite the NATO nations, strengthen the alliance, and prevent the proliferation of nuclear capability by individual countries. The practical consideration of cost is also important. Since many of the NATO countries cannot afford the cost of developing an independent nuclear force, MLF would give them a chance to participate without great expense.

The highest policy-making group controlling the MLF might be a board of governors with a representative from each nation. A director-general would be responsible for carrying out policies of the board, and for procurement and administration. The senior officer of the MLF would be the force commander, who would report to the director-general. The entire operational and support establishment would require an estimated seventy-three-hundred people, military and civilians.

All of the ships, equipment, weapons, and facilities would be jointly owned by all participating nations. The multilateral concept would apply to ownership, financial support, and decisions concerning the MLF.

Some of those opposed to the MLF doubt the feasibility of mixed-manning of ships; question the vulnerability of surface missile ships carrying Polaris; disparage its usefulness; and doubt whether a satisfactory control procedure could be agreed upon. Any new concept as revolutionary as the MLF is bound to have pros and cons, and the doubts raised serve to sharpen the concept of the MLF, and might help to shape the force into an effective nuclear deterrent.

The mixed-manning of ships is certainly not a new idea. It has a notable example of success in Lord Nelson's flagship, HMS *Victory*, at Trafalgar, and is more often the rule than the exception in the merchantmen now plying the world's sea lanes. To further demonstrate the feasibility of mixed-manning, the modern, complex, guided-missile destroyer USS *Claude V. Ricketts* was manned by personnel from six nations, in addition to those from the United States. Represented were Great Britain, Germany, Greece, Italy, Turkey, and the Netherlands. The crew members from foreign navies first reported on board in mid-May, 1964, in Norfolk, Virginia.

By the end of the year, the foreign and U.S. officers and men formed an efficient ship's company, with a fine esprit de corps. Working together, the crew from various NATO nations proved the value of harmoniously cooperating on a day-to-day basis, a demonstrably better way to foster international friendship than give-away programs. USS *Claude V. Ricketts* gave manifest evidence that mixed-manning is feasible, and can produce excellent results.

The vulnerability of MLF ships is not as great as one might think. The twenty-five ships of the Force would resemble the typical merchant cargo ships, numbering three to four thousand, in the proposed area of operation. If trailed by submarines, they could easily elude them by steaming into shoal areas along the European littoral. MLF ships would have sufficient speed to outrun most surface ships, and they could join friendly surface formations to lose would-be trackers posing as trawlers, or using some other old trick of the sea.

Aircraft trailing an MLF ship would have difficulty operating over friendly countries, particularly in coastal waters. The NATO countries form an almost solid land barrier between the communist bloc and the sea areas of operation. From an aircraft, difficulties of distinguishing an MLF ship from any one of thousands of merchantmen is readily apparent. Aircraft could not remain over a ship for a sustained period, and the need for refueling, the darkness of night, fog, and bad weather, all add to the problems of air tracking. Furthermore, a ship is a mobile missile launching base which, by morning's light, can be far removed from its plotted position at sundown.

The usefulness of the MLF cannot be seriously questioned, since it would consist of a powerful force of two hundred Polaris missiles, dispersed over a large area. As a retaliatory force, it would not endanger the heavily populated areas of Europe. Land-based missile launching sites not only attract surprise, first-strike destruction, they are easily processed by enemy target computers.

The MLF would provide a different type of delivery which would prevent a worrisome and expensive counter-effort by an enemy. As conceived, the MLF would not replace or duplicate national or NATO forces in being. It would complement the land and sea-based missiles and aircraft already in existence, adding diversity and strength to NATO.

Of course, the question of control, or who "pulls the trigger," is a complicated matter. The "green light" to fire the weapons would require the concurrence of the United States and all other participants. Authority to use the missiles would then be released, to be fired in coordination with other means of delivering nuclear weapons.

The MLF, it is true, might not be the ultimate answer to offsetting the massive nuclear threat posed by the Communist bloc. However, it was a sound proposal offered to the other members of NATO, and a number of details were open for discussion. It is by no means being forced upon the NATO membership, but the fact remains that a better solution has not been suggested.

President de Gaulle, with a perversity hard to match in history, reacted to the MLF proposal in a manner most pleasing to the Communist bloc. He considered the MLF a threat to the continuation of NATO, and an attempt by the United States to dominate the affairs of Europe. The de Gaulle government, however antagonistic over U.S. proposals, cannot ignore the facts of life in the nuclear age.

The precious quality of unity in NATO is more important than any one force, man, or nation. If MLF is not accepted, some other idea must be proposed, agreed upon, and made to work. Unity should not wait, because time cannot.

The "Sword of Damocles," now hanging over the major powers of the world, is the danger of a massive nuclear exchange. The tenuous thread of peace by which this "sword" hangs is uncomfortably thin. Man's ingenuity has devised the tremendous explosive power of nuclear fission and fusion. His ingenuity thus far has fallen short in devising a reliable means of controlling the nuclear explosives of his invention.

The late President Kennedy, speaking to the National Academy of Sciences in October, 1963, said: "Every time you scientists make a major invention, we politicians have to invent a new institution to cope with it—and almost invariably, these days, it must be an international institution." This statement reflects the scientific outburst since World War II in atomic weapons, peaceful uses for nuclear energy, space exploration, oceanography, and other fields.

One of the most pressing matters resulting from the emergence of nuclear energy was the matter of international control. Although banning the use of nuclear weapons through international agreement seems a long way off, there has been agreement on a partial nuclear test ban. The governments of the United States, Great Britain, and the U.S.S.R. signed a treaty on July 25, 1963, to prohibit any nuclear weapon test explosion in the atmosphere, in outer space, or underwater. Tests were permitted underground with the proviso that such explosions should not carry any radioactive debris outside the territorial limits of the country conducting the tests.

In a speech proclaiming this treaty, President Kennedy pointed out that "it will not resolve all conflicts, or cause the Communists to forego their ambitions, or eliminate the dangers of war. It will not reduce our need for arms, or allies, or programs of assistance to others. But it is an important first step."

When the next positive step will be taken is difficult to predict. We can only note with apprehension the proliferation of nuclear weapons. Countries with nuclear capabilities are increasing their nuclear stockpiles, and the number of nations having nuclear weapons at their disposal is growing. Unfortunately, two of these countries are Russia and Red China—a circumstance certain to render any agreement on the non-use of nuclear weapons difficult, if not hopeless.

The President's Evaluation Committee, following the underwater test of Operation Crossroads in 1946, reported in part: "To us, who have witnessed the devastating effects of these tests, it is evident that if there is to be any security or safety in the world, war must be eliminated as a means of settling differences among nations."

As the decades pass, the force of this statement will grow as the stockpile of nuclear weapons also grows. We can only hope that the world will apply itself more to the peaceful applications of nuclear energy in the future. Project Plowshare, a program to promote the peaceful uses of nuclear energy, is an example of directing our efforts to serve mankind rather than to destroy him.

The Shippingport Power Plant, supplying electricity for the city of Pittsburgh, is a milestone in applying nuclear energy for useful purposes. Admiral Rickover's fame in seagoing reactors may have obscured his splendid achievement and dynamic leadership in helping to make this contribution to the electrical industry. Working in cooperation with the AEC and industry, he made a monumental contribution to the technology of nuclear power plant operation in the United States and abroad.

Other Plowshare-type applications of nuclear energy cover a wide variety of uses. Earth-moving operations may soon be applied to help build a canal to replace the old Panama Canal; to open mountain passes for highways and railroads; and to help exploit mining resources. Nuclear medicine, food processing, and water desalinization are other areas where nuclear energy will help to provide benefits leading toward a better life. However, enjoyment of a more abundant life will not be complete until the problem of controlling nuclear weapons is solved.

The awakening of the nuclear age inexorably has led us to the sea as a medium for the application of nuclear propulsion. The vast oceans offer the best medium for waging nuclear warfare, for launching missiles, and, at the same time, afford the best protective concealment against nuclear surprise or retaliation. Nuclear submarines cannot be seen, photographed, or picked up on radar. Their battle areas, when photographed, show only empty, wave-tossed wastelands from horizon to horizon.

It is little wonder then that the United States should start looking to the seas for exploitation on a scale never before known. Realizing the fabulous resources available in our saltwater frontier, oceanography in the nuclear era must be furthered without delay. If our effort in exploring the oceans were on a par with our effort in space exploration, the return would stagger the imagination. In the prenuclear era, a vigorous program of oceanography was highly desirable. The age of the atom has made it imperative.

We can measure the strength of our future sea power, not only by the number of ships, aircraft, missiles, and men, but by the number of active, vital research programs which we are supporting. These are essential if we are to remain the world's leading power on the seas. The U.S. Navy, now in the vanguard of nuclear development, must continue to share progress with science and industry. Only through mutual support will our sea power continue to meet the challenges in national defense which the future may impose upon our nuclear Navy.

Glossary

AAM: air-to-air missile

AEC: Atomic Energy Commission

AFRRI: Armed Forces Radiobiology Research Institute

ALUMINAUT: a commercial submarine designed for exploitation of undersea resources

ALVIN: a two-man research vehicle for submarine research

Aquanaut: one who is trained and equipped to remain for prolonged periods in the ocean depths

ASM: air-to-surface missile

ASROC: an antisubmarine weapon fired by rocket from a surface ship

ASTOR: a fast, long-range electric torpedo

ASW: antisubmarine warfare

AUM: air-to-underwater missile

Beam rider: a missile guided toward its target by a radar beam

Brought critical: said of a nuclear reactor when a sustained nuclear reaction has been achieved

CAP: Combat Air Patrol

CGN: designation for nuclear-powered, guided-missile cruiser

CIC: Combat Information Center

CTR: controlled thermonuclear reaction

CVAN: designation for nuclear-powered, attack aircraft carrier

CVS: an aircraft carrier whose air group is composed of ASW planes, usually the flagship of a HUK group

DASA: Defense Atomic Support Agency

Glossary

DASH: Destroyer Antisubmarine Helicopter used to deliver an anti-submarine weapon from a specially configured destroyer equipped with a landing deck

Destroyer Leader: a naval ship larger than a destroyer but smaller than a cruiser (also called frigate)

DLGN: designation for nuclear-powered, guided-missile frigate; the "DL" is a carry-over from the initial designation of "destroyer leader"

DOLPHIN: an experimental submarine for developing deeper-diving, quieter submarines

Drone aircraft: radio-controlled aircraft

Drone boats: radio-controlled boats and small craft

DTMB: David Taylor Model Basin, Washington, D. C.

ESP: electrostatic precipitator for removing aerosol contaminants in submarines

FBM: Fleet Ballistic Missile

Fission products: the complex mixture of substances produced as a result of nuclear fission

FLIP: a stable platform for accurate acoustic and electromagnetic measurements at various locations in the ocean

Frigate: a ship of the U.S. Navy between the size of a destroyer and a cruiser (initially designated as a destroyer leader)

Guided missiles: missiles guided during flight by radar, radio, thermal attraction, or some other influence

HICAPCOM: high capacity communications system

HUK group: a hunter-killer group of mixed ASW elements

Hydrofoils: blades upon which the hulls of waterborne craft can rise free of the surface at high speeds

Isotopes: two or more forms of the same element having the same number of protons with different numbers of neutrons in their nuclei

[191]

JCAE: Joint Committee for Atomic Energy (congressional)

Kiloton: one thousand tons

LINAC: an electron linear accelerator

Mach: the speed of sound; Mach two = twice the speed of sound

MAD gear: Magnetic Anomaly Detection equipment using interruptions in the earth's magnetic lines of force to detect submarines

Megaton: one million tons

MLF: MultiLateral Force; proposed force of Polaris-firing surface ships manned by personnel from NATO countries

NASA: National Aeronautics and Space Administration

NATO: North Atlantic Treaty Organization

NBC: Nuclear, Biological and Chemical

NEL: Naval Electronics Laboratory at Point Loma, San Diego

NEWS: Naval Electronic Warfare Simulator

NMFRL: Naval Medical Field Research Laboratory

NMRI: Naval Medical Research Institute

NNMC: National Naval Medical Center, Bethesda, Maryland

NOL: Naval Ordnance Laboratory, White Oaks, Maryland

NOMAD: Navy Oceanographic (and) Meteorological Automatic Device

NOTS: Naval Ordnance Test Station, China Lake, California

NRDL: Naval Radiological Defense Laboratory, San Francisco, California

NRL: Naval Research Laboratory, Washington, D. C.

NTDS: Naval Tactical Data System; a high-speed computer and communication system

OMEGA: a long-range navigation system using very low frequency radio signals

ONR: Office of Naval Research, Washington, D. C.

PERT: Program Evaluation and Review Technique; a management

technique applied to complex and critically time-phased projects

Plasma: a gaseous state of matter in which the particles have a high internal energy level (kinetic or thermal) and are free to move and collide

Plutonium: a fissionable element used in nuclear explosives

Polynya: an opening or thin spot in thick arctic ice through which a nuclear submarine can surface

PPI: Plan Position Indicator; a radar scope which indicates the relative position of other ships, or objects, to one's own ship

Project Plowshare: a program to foster the peaceful applications of nuclear power

Project Sherwood: an AEC project to develop a useful, controlled thermonuclear reaction

Propellant: a liquid or solid type of fuel used to propel a weapon toward a target

Proximity fuze: a fuze designed to detonate an explosive charge near a target

Reactor: a mechanism which provides energy through a controlled nuclear reaction

REEL: Radiation Exposure Evaluation Laboratory

Rem: a unit of ionizing radiation dose which has the biological equivalent of one roentgen of X ray or gamma radiation at a given energy

SAM: surface-to-air missile

Seabees: nickname for Naval Construction Battalions (CBs), or the men who serve in them

Sealab: an underwater station where divers can remain for days without surfacing

SINS: Ship's Inertial Navigation System; a complex device which gives a constant, accurate position

SNAP: Systems for Nuclear Auxiliary Power

SPAR: a seagoing platform for acoustic research

Special Projects: The organization charged with developing and improving the Polaris FBM system

SSM: surface-to-surface missile

STR: Submarine Thermal Reactor

SUBROC: a submarine-fired rocket which projects a homing torpedo some distance through the air to re-enter the water and destroy an opposing submarine

SUM: surface-to-underwater missile

TENOC: a ten-year program in oceanography

Thermonuclear reaction: a nuclear fusion reaction brought about by extremely high temperatures

"Top off": to fill the fuel bunkers

TRIESTE: a bathyscaphe or deep-diving ocean research vehicle

TRIGA: a research reactor which takes its name from Training, Research, Isotope production, General Atomic

U-235: a fissionable isotope of uranium

USM: underwater-to-surface missile

UUM: underwater-to-underwater missile

VDS: variable depth sonar device lowered from a destroyer to various depths to detect submarines

Warhead: the explosive charge of a weapon designed to detonate on a target

Yield: used to describe the power of a nuclear explosive

Index

⚓

Are you getting _all_ your library offers you? ---

IN
> Books
>> Magazines
>> Newspapers
>> Pamphlets
>>> Government Documents
>> Pictures
>> Maps
>>> Phonograph Records
>> Sheet Music
>> Story Hours
>>> Information Service